marscademy.com

(videos, topic-based questions, exam papers and much more)

Published by MarsCademy Publishing

Copyright © 2023 Marsida Horeshka

Proofreader: Magdalena Galka

With special thanks to Sunjeong Shin for her support and wisdom.

ISBN: 978-1-915811-02-8

1 About the author

Hello there! I'm Marsida Horeshka, but you can call me Mars, just like the planet – hence the name MarsMaths. With over a decade of experience in the education sector, including several years as a subject leader and manager, I've dedicated my career to making maths more accessible and enjoyable for everyone.

You might already know me from my YouTube channel, Mars Maths, where I post educational videos to help demystify complex maths concepts. I also regularly update my website, marscademy.com, with a variety of resources, including practice questions, answers, and step-by-step solutions to exam papers. I'm constantly adding new content, so be sure to check in regularly for the latest updates.

I'm thrilled to have you join me on this mathematical journey. Together, we'll explore the fascinating world of maths and discover the power and beauty of numbers.

2 About the book

Start by identifying the areas you want to improve. Study the topic, practice the exercises and check your answers. If you need further explanation, you can find my detailed video tutorials on YouTube. Just search for the topic followed by 'Mars Maths'.
Here's what you can expect from this book:

- Step-by-step Explanations
- Visual Representations
- Revisiting Earlier Topics
- Practice Questions
- Practice Paper

This book is designed to help you understand, apply and master maths.

3 You can

It is quite common to feel like you're not doing very well in maths or that you are not a 'maths person'. What I can say is that you're not the only one experiencing these feelings towards maths. If you want to do maths, then you CAN do maths. There is nothing to stop you. Scientific evidence shows that there is no such thing as a 'maths person' and anyone can do maths.
Struggling to complete a maths task though, is a good thing. You are learning if you struggle and if something was too easy, we wouldn't be doing it anyway. Why would we?

Challenge yourself to achieve L2, the level required for many jobs and further/higher education studies. I absolutely believe that you can. Can you? **I challenge you.** And once you've passed your exam, come and tell me on YouTube or social media. I'd love to celebrate your success.

Self-assessment

Add your confidence level (1 to 5) for each topic before you start studying the topic and when you finish. 1 is the lowest level and 5 is the highest.

	start	end
Number		
Read and write numbers up to 200	☐	☐
Order and compare numbers up to 200	☐	☐
Count in ones up to 100	☐	☐
Count in twos up to 100	☐	☐
Count in tens, twenties and fives, up to 100	☐	☐
Recognise and sequence odd and even numbers up to 100	☐	☐
Add two-digit numbers	☐	☐
Subtract two-digit numbers	☐	☐
Multiply whole numbers up to 12 x 12	☐	☐
Divide two-digit by one-digit whole numbers	☐	☐
Use symbols: + , - , x , ÷ , =	☐	☐
Recognise simple fractions	☐	☐
Read, write and use decimals to one decimal place	☐	☐
Measures, Shape and Space		
Calculate money with pounds and pence	☐	☐
Know the number of hours in a day and be able to sequence them	☐	☐
Know the number of months in a year and weeks in a year	☐	☐
Read time in hours, half hours and quarter hours	☐	☐
Use millimetres, centimetres, metres and kilometres	☐	☐
Use grams and kilograms	☐	☐
Use millilitres and litres	☐	☐
Read and compare temperatures	☐	☐
Read and use scales to the nearest labelled divisions	☐	☐
Recognise 2D and 3Dshapes	☐	☐
Describe properties of 2D and 3D shapes	☐	☐
Use simple positional vocabulary	☐	☐
Handling Data		
Extract information from lists	☐	☐
Extract information from tables	☐	☐
Extract information from diagrams	☐	☐
Extract information from bar charts	☐	☐
Sort objects using two criteria	☐	☐
Make numerical comparisons from bar charts	☐	☐
Take information from one format and represent it in another	☐	☐
Practice Paper	☐	☐

CONTENTS

Read, write, order and compare numbers up to 200

We use numbers when:
- ➢ catching a bus
- ➢ writing the home address
- ➢ reading speed limits
- ➢ comparing prices
- ➢ buying and selling items
- ➢ paying bills
- ➢ measuring ingredients

Read and write numbers up to 100

These are the numbers from 1 to 100.

1 one	2 two	3 three	4 four	5 five	6 six	7 seven	8 eight	9 nine	10 ten
11 eleven	12 twelve	13 thirteen	14 fourteen	15 fifteen	16 sixteen	17 seventeen	18 eighteen	19 nineteen	20 twenty
21 twenty one	22 twenty two	23 twenty three	24 twenty four	25 twenty five	26 twenty six	27 twenty seven	28 twenty eight	29 twenty nine	30 thirty
31 thirty one	32 thirty two	33 thirty three	34 thirty four	35 thirty five	36 thirty six	37 thirty seven	38 thirty eight	39 thirty nine	40 forty
41 forty one	42 forty two	43 forty three	44 forty four	45 forty five	46 forty six	47 forty seven	48 forty eight	49 forty nine	50 fifty
51 fifty one	52 fifty two	53 fifty three	54 fifty four	55 fifty five	56 fifty six	57 fifty seven	58 fifty eight	59 fifty nine	60 sixty
61 sixty one	62 sixty two	63 sixty three	64 sixty four	65 sixty five	66 sixty six	67 sixty seven	68 sixty eight	69 sixty nine	70 seventy
71 seventy one	72 seventy two	73 seventy three	74 seventy four	75 seventy five	76 seventy six	77 seventy seven	78 seventy eight	79 seventy nine	80 eighty
81 eighty one	82 eighty two	83 eighty three	84 eighty four	85 eighty five	86 eighty six	87 eighty seven	88 eighty eight	89 eighty nine	90 ninety
91 ninety one	92 ninety two	93 ninety three	94 ninety four	95 ninety five	96 ninety six	97 ninety seven	98 ninety eight	99 ninety nine	100 one

What do you notice in every **row**?

1	2	3	4	5	6	7	8	9	10
11	12	13	14	15	16	17	18	19	20
21	22	23	24	25	26	27	28	29	30
31	32	33	34	35	36	37	38	39	40
41	42	43	44	45	46	47	48	49	50
51	52	53	54	55	56	57	58	59	60
61	62	63	64	65	66	67	68	69	70
71	72	73	74	75	76	77	78	79	80
81	82	83	84	85	86	87	88	89	90
91	92	93	94	95	96	97	98	99	100

The ones have the same pattern: 1, 2, 3, 4, 5, 6, 7, 8, 9, 0.

What do you notice in every **column**?

1	2	3	4	5	6	7	8	9	10
11	12	13	14	15	16	17	18	19	20
21	22	23	24	25	26	27	28	29	30
31	32	33	34	35	36	37	38	39	40
41	42	43	44	45	46	47	48	49	50
51	52	53	54	55	56	57	58	59	60
61	62	63	64	65	66	67	68	69	70
71	72	73	74	75	76	77	78	79	80
81	82	83	84	85	86	87	88	89	90
91	92	93	94	95	96	97	98	99	100

The ones stay the same: **1**, 1**1**, 2**1**, 3**1**, 4**1**, 5**1**, 6**1**, 7**1**, 8**1**, 9**1**. The tens change.

1 Fill this table with the numbers up to 100.

1									10
91									100

2 Fill the gaps.

	2		4		6		8		10
	12		14		16		18		20
	22		24		26		28		30
	32		34		36		38		40
	42		44		46		48		50
	52		54		56		58		60
	62		64		66		68		70
	72		74		76		78		80
	82		84		86		88		90
	92		94		96		98		100

 Write numbers up to 100 on a piece of paper and look at them often until you know them by heart.

3 Fill the gaps.

1		3		5		7		9	
	12		14		16		18		20
21		23		25		27		29	
	32		34		36		38		40
41		43		45		47		49	
	52		54		56		58		60
61		63		65		67		69	
	72		74		76		78		80
81		83		85		87		89	
	92		94		96		98		100

4 Fill the gaps **in words**.

one									ten
ninety one									one hundred

Here are the numbers from 0 to 30 represented.

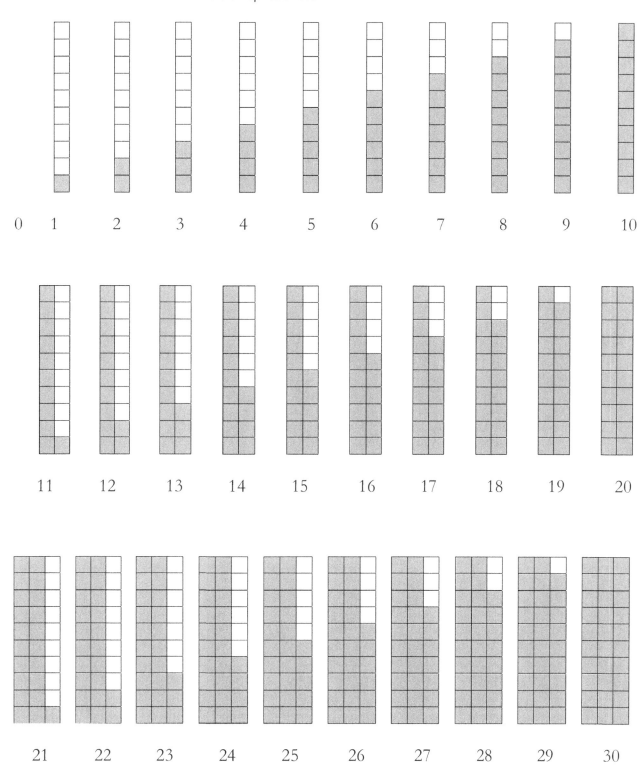

What do you notice?

In each row, the numbers go up by one: 2**1**, 2**2**, 2**3** …

In each column, the numbers go up by ten: **1**, **1**1, **2**1 …

Here are the **tens** being represented, from 10 to 100.

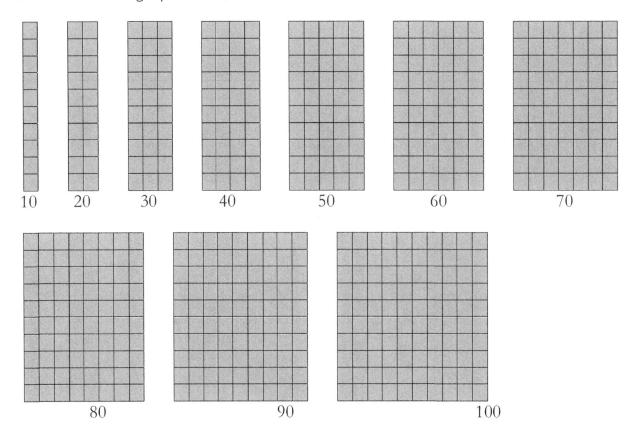

10   20   30   40   50   60   70

80   90   100

What do you notice?

One block of 10 is added each time.

These are the numbers from 101 to 130.

101 one hundred and one	102 one hundred and two	103 one hundred and three	104 one hundred and four	105 one hundred and five	106 one hundred and six	107 one hundred and seven	108 one hundred and eight	109 one hundred and nine	110 one hundred and ten
111 one hundred and eleven	112 one hundred and twelve	113 one hundred and thirteen	114 one hundred and fourteen	115 one hundred and fifteen	116 one hundred and sixteen	117 one hundred and seventeen	118 one hundred and eighteen	119 one hundred and nineteen	120 one hundred and twenty
121 one hundred and twenty one	122 one hundred and twenty two	123 one hundred and twenty three	124 one hundred and twenty four	125 one hundred and twenty five	126 one hundred and twenty six	127 one hundred and twenty seven	128 one hundred and twenty eight	129 one hundred and twenty nine	130 one hundred and thirty

Then we go to 131, 132, 133, 134, 135, 136, 137, 138, 139, 140, 141 … 199, 200.

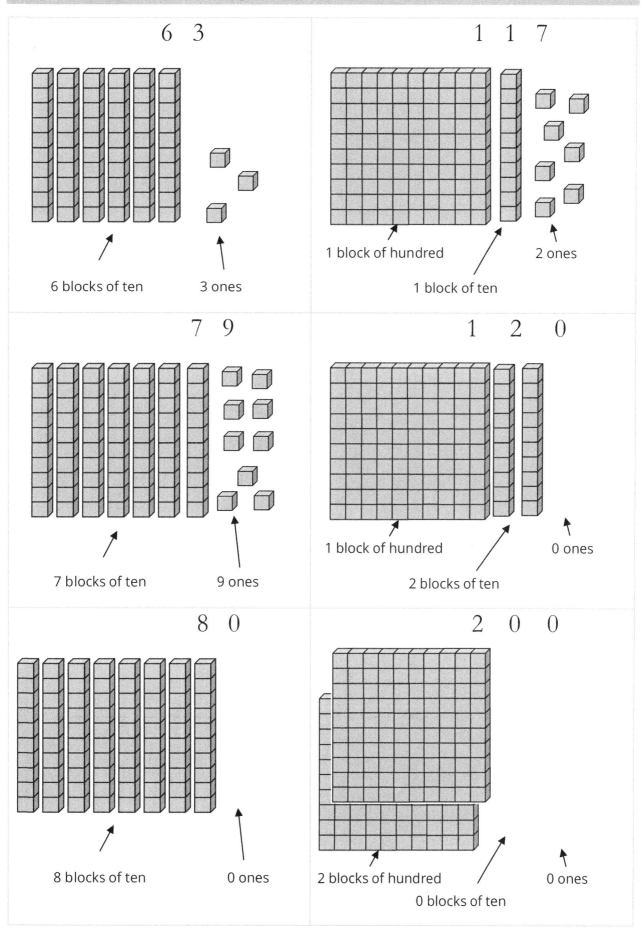

6   3

6 blocks of ten   3 ones

1   1   7

1 block of hundred   2 ones

1 block of ten

7   9

7 blocks of ten   9 ones

1   2   0

1 block of hundred   0 ones

2 blocks of ten

8   0

8 blocks of ten   0 ones

2   0   0

2 blocks of hundred   0 ones

0 blocks of ten

Another name for **ones** is **units**.
Number 14 has **a block of 10** and **4 units.** Number 18 has **a block of 10** and **8 units.**

Examples:

<u>69</u> is a **number.**	<u>197</u> is a **number.**	<u>108</u> is a **number.**
This number has **two digits:**	This number has **three digits:**	This number has **three digits:**
6 represents **60**	**1** represents **100**	**1** represents **100**
9 represents **9**	**9** represents **90**	**8** represents **8**
	7 represents **7**	

5 ▷ Numbers 68 and 150 have been added to the grid below.

Hundreds	Tens	Units
	6	8
1	5	0

Add these numbers to the grid: 39, 47, 102, 158, 200, 7, 119, 99, 171

6 ▷ a) Write the number that has three tens and five ones. _____
b) Write the number that has seven tens and zero ones. _____

Another two words that mean the same as **digits** are **figures** and **numerals.**

12

7 Fill the gaps in digits.

1									10
11									
21									
31									
41									
51									
61									
71									
81									
91									100

101									110
111									
121									
131									
141									
151									
161									
171									
181									
191									200

8 Write these numbers in **digits**.

twenty _____	one hundred and eleven _____	ninety nine _____
thirty nine _____	one hundred and twenty _____	one hundred and seventy one _____
seventy four _____	one hundred and sixty _____	one hundred and eighteen _____
eighty _____	one hundred and seventy five _____	one hundred and twenty four _____
forty seven _____	one hundred and thirty four _____	one hundred and seven _____
ninety five _____	one hundred and eighty six _____	two hundred _____

9 Write these numbers in **words**.

67 _____

113 _____

190 _____

200 _____

107 _____

138 _____

109 _____

172 _____

101 _____

10 Add the missing numbers. The first one has been done for you.

The Bank App

Amount you are sending in digits:

£ 138

in words:
one hundred and
thirty eight
____pounds

The Bank App

Amount you are sending in digits:

£_____

in words:
one hundred and
nineteen
____pounds

The Bank App

Amount you are sending in digits:

£_____

in words:
two hundred
_____
___pounds

The Bank App

Amount you are sending in digits:

£ 189

in words:
_____
_____
____pounds

The Bank App

Amount you are sending in digits:

£ 107

in words:
_____
_____
____pounds

The Bank App

Amount you are sending in digits:

£ 144

in words:
_____
_____
____pounds

11 Sally is turning 48 next week. Write 48 in words.

_____

12 Zoe writes 88 as **eigty eigt**. Write number 88 correctly in words.

_____

13 Asha is playing a game online. This is how many points she has.
How many points does she have, in words?

_____

14 ⟩ Three people got these cakes on their birthdays. Fill these gaps by writing numbers **in words**.

| Heather | Jasi | Enes |

Jasi is _____ years old.

Heather is _____ years older than Enes.

How old will Enes be in two years' time? _____

15 ⟩ Hamza is waiting for bus **sixty seven**. Tick the bus he is waiting for.

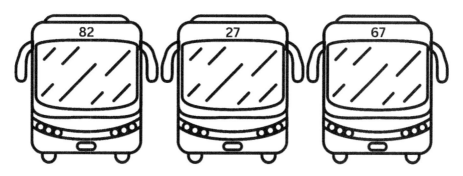

16 ⟩ Lou is visiting her friend. The address is **90 Soho Road**.

She knocks on this door on Soho Road. Is this the correct one?

_____

_____

17 ⟩ Roi pays **one hundred and thirty five pounds** rent a week. Write the amount in numerals.

Rent   _____

18 ⟩ Les is taking out a loan. He will pay back **one hundred ninety eight** pounds every week.
Write this amount in digits.

_____

Progress check

1 ▷ Numbers 68 and 150 have been added to the grid below.

Hundreds	Tens	Units
	6	8
1	5	0

Add these numbers to the grid: 141, 35, 60, 108, 100, 9

2 ▷ Match these numbers with the words that represent them.

17		one hundred
100		sixty eight
111		one hundred and eleven
68		seventeen

3 ▷ Ayla writes the number 18 as 'eighty'. Is she right? Explain your answer.

_____

4 ▷ How do you write the number 55 in words?

_____

5 ▷ Jane fills in the cheque below. Write the amount in digits in the cheque.

The Bank
Pay_Joe Bloggs_____   £ [   ]
one hundred and twenty pounds only

Order and compare numbers up to 200

Greater and **smaller**

Here are the numbers from 0 to 100 on a number line.

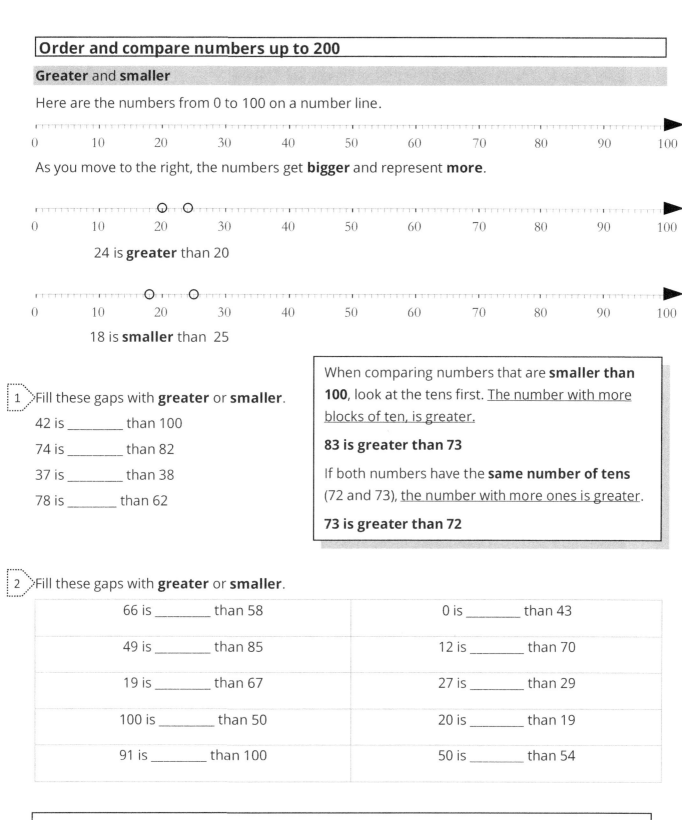

As you move to the right, the numbers get **bigger** and represent **more**.

24 is **greater** than 20

18 is **smaller** than 25

When comparing numbers that are **smaller than 100**, look at the tens first. The number with more blocks of ten, is greater.

83 is greater than 73

If both numbers have the **same number of tens** (72 and 73), the number with more ones is greater.

73 is greater than 72

1 > Fill these gaps with **greater** or **smaller**.

42 is _____ than 100

74 is _____ than 82

37 is _____ than 38

78 is _____ than 62

2 > Fill these gaps with **greater** or **smaller**.

66 is _____ than 58	0 is _____ than 43
49 is _____ than 85	12 is _____ than 70
19 is _____ than 67	27 is _____ than 29
100 is _____ than 50	20 is _____ than 19
91 is _____ than 100	50 is _____ than 54

When comparing **numbers that are greater than 100 with numbers that are smaller than 100**, the number that is greater than 100 is greater than the other one: **183 is greater than 83**

If **both numbers are greater than 100**, the number with more tens is greater: **183 is greater than 173**

If **both numbers are greater than 100** and **they have the same number of tens**, the number with more ones is greater: **183 is greater than 182**

3 Fill these gaps with **greater** or **smaller**.

119 is _____ than 100	109 is _____ than 110
160 is _____ than 130	190 is _____ than 180
108 is _____ than 180	109 is _____ than 120
17 is _____ than 117	160 is _____ than 159
100 is _____ than 101	130 is _____ than 0

Higher is another word for **greater**.
Lower is another word for **smaller**.

4 Complete these sentences using **higher** or **lower**.

29 is _____ than 129	200 is _____ than 199
115 is _____ than 150	159 is _____ than 155
108 is _____ than 140	169 is _____ than 200
170 is _____ than 194	186 is _____ than 194
0 is _____ than 176	135 is _____ than 116

5 Find a number that is greater than 76. _____

6 Find a number that is smaller than 160. _____

7 Find a number that is greater than 76 but smaller than 160. _____

8 Jo is shopping for size 22 dresses. Will size 16 fit? Why?

_____

9 Miguel has £50 in his wallet. A coat costs £67. Can he afford the coat?

_____

10 Write a number that is greater than 99. _____

11 Write a number that is smaller than 80. _____

12 Write a number that is greater than 80 but smaller than 99. _____

Greatest and smallest

Out of **30**, **45** and **64**, 30 is **the smallest** as it is the first in the number line.

0	10	20	30	40	50	60	70	80	90	100

Out of **51**, **26** and **38**, 51 is **the greatest** as it is the last in the number line.

0	10	20	30	40	50	60	70	80	90	100

13 ▷ Fill the gaps.

Out of **37**, **40** and **54**, ___ is **the smallest** and ___ is **the greatest**.

0	10	20	30	40	50	60	70	80	90	100

Out of **67**, **53** and **100**, ___ is **the smallest** and ___ is **the greatest**.

0	10	20	30	40	50	60	70	80	90	100

Out of **92**, **90** and **86**, ___ is **the smallest** and ___ is **the greatest**.

0	10	20	30	40	50	60	70	80	90	100

Out of **39**, **0** and **44**, ___ is **the smallest** and ___ is **the greatest**.

0	10	20	30	40	50	60	70	80	90	100

Out of **58**, **72** and **82**, ___ is **the smallest** and ___ is **the greatest**.

0	10	20	30	40	50	60	70	80	90	100

Out of **66**, **16** and **60**, ___ is **the smallest** and ___ is **the greatest**.

0	10	20	30	40	50	60	70	80	90	100

Out of **78**, **41** and **29**, ___ is **the smallest** and ___ is **the greatest**.

0	10	20	30	40	50	60	70	80	90	100

14 a) Circle the number that is the **greatest**:
90,   65,   8,   67

f) Circle the number that is the **smallest**:
60,   124,   102,   99

b) Circle the number that is the **greatest**:
167,   190,   183,   195

g) Circle the number that is the **smallest**:
108,   118,   180,   18

c) Circle the number that is the **greatest**:
102,   156,   198,   173

h) Circle the number that is the **smallest**:
185,   100,   177,   159

d) Circle the number that is the **greatest**:
0,   159,   98,   160

i) Circle the number that is the **smallest**:
194,   138,   74,   145

e) Circle the number that is the **greatest**:
196,   188,   129,   167

j) Circle the number that is the **smallest**:
178,   111,   105,   134

15 Put these numbers in order, **starting with the smallest**.

a) 84, 57, 103   _____, _____, _____

b) 163, 196, 200   _____, _____, _____

c) 89, 40, 104   _____, _____, _____

d) 92, 167, 185   _____, _____, _____

e) 174, 187, 153   _____, _____, _____

f) 184, 186, 153   _____, _____, _____

g) 169, 170, 171   _____, _____, _____

h) 134, 177, 110   _____, _____, _____

16 Put these numbers in order, **starting with the greatest**.

a) 192, 167, 191   _____, _____, _____

b) 174, 180, 195   _____, _____, _____

c) 172, 100, 120   _____, _____, _____

d) 99, 100, 108   _____, _____, _____

e) 200, 20, 120   _____, _____, _____

f) 118, 180, 108   _____, _____, _____

g) 169, 145, 137   _____, _____, _____

h) 1, 180, 137   _____, _____, _____

Ascending is another word for **increasing** or ordering from **the lowest to the highest**.
Descending is another word for **decreasing** or ordering from **the highest to the lowest**.

Example: 81, 37, 153, 19

Increasing order: 19, 37, 81, 153

Decreasing order: 153, 81, 37, 19

Key Words

---

17 a) Put these numbers in ascending order: 31, 53, 82, 23: _____, _____, _____, _____

b) Put these numbers in ascending order: 67, 188, 107, 49: _____, _____, _____, _____

c) Put these numbers in ascending order: 142, 95, 162, 58: _____, _____, _____, _____

d) Put these numbers in descending order: 71, 133, 26, 119: _____, _____, _____, _____

e) Put these numbers in descending order: 164, 145, 139, 108: _____, _____, _____, _____

f) Put these numbers in descending order: 91, 108, 120, 162: _____, _____, _____, _____

18) Sonia is looking for a cheap flight to Spain. These are the prices of the tickets she found online.

Ticket A	Ticket B	Ticket C	Ticket D
£83	£96	£102	£97

a) Which ticket is the cheapest? _____

b) Put the tickets in order, starting with the cheapest: _____, _____, _____, _____

19) Put these measurements in order starting with the longest:　78m　170m　80m　187m

_____, _____, _____, _____

20) Fey wants to buy a bag of dishwasher tablets. She wants to buy the bag with the highest number of tablets in it. Tick the bag Fey will buy.

Bag A	Bag B	Bag C	Bag D
100 tablets	108 tablets	112 tablets	65 tablets

21) Asma works in different offices during the week. This is how long it takes her to travel to each office.

Office A	Office B	Office C	Office D
25 minutes	37 minutes	29 minutes	42 minutes

a) Which office is closest to Asma's house? _____

b) Put the office in order, starting with the one that takes the shortest time to travel to:
_____, _____, _____, _____

22) Asma wants to buy a coat. She will buy the cheapest one.

£41　£34　£57　£52

a) Tick the coat Asma will buy.
b) Put these prices in order, starting with the cheapest:　£_____, £_____, £_____, £_____

23) Maria is driving on the motorway at 57 miles per hour.
This is the speed limit on the motorway.
Is Maria within the speed limit?

60

_____

Progress check

1 > Put these amounts in order, starting with the one with the highest value.

£108   £18   £180   £81

_____, _____, _____, _____

2 > a) Write the amounts in digits on the cheques.

The Bank

Pay _Joe Bloggs_____

one hundred and twenty pounds only   £

The Bank

Pay _Joe Bloggs_____

one hundred and two pounds only   £

b) Which of these cheques has the highest value? Tick it.

3 > Susan ordered some numbers from the lowest to the highest: 18, 91, 72, 103, 105. Is she correct? Why?

_____

4 > Here is the time it takes Andy to travel to college.

By bus **30 minutes**

Walk **85 minutes**

By bike **45 minutes**

Andy wants to go to college in the shortest time possible. Should he use a bike, the bus or walk?

_____

5 > Aaron says: 'Eighty is bigger than eighteen'. Is Aaron correct? Explain your answer.

_____

Count reliably up to 100 items

We count:
- ➢ fruit and vegetables
- ➢ plates, spoons and forks
- ➢ money notes and coins
- ➢ minutes and hours
- ➢ followers or views
- ➢ pens, pencils and books
- ➢ days and years
- ➢ calories
- ➢ points or scores in a game

Count in ones up to 100

1 ⟩ Fill in the gaps in these patterns.

25		27		29		31			
	51		53				57		
88	89			93					
		67	69						
61									70
	42				46				

2 ⟩ a) What number comes after 67? _____   e) What number comes before 1? _____

b) What number comes before 80? _____   f) Write a number that is between 49 and 51. ____

c) Write a number that is between 46 and 49. ____   g) What is one more than 99? _____

d) What number comes before 100? _____   h) What is one less than 90? _____

3 ⟩ Fill these gaps.

21, ___, 23, ___, 25, ___, 27, ___, 29, ___

30, 31, ___, 33, ___, 35, ___, 37, ___

41, 42, ___, 44, 45, ___, 47, 48, ___, ___

65, 66, 67, ___, ___, 70, ___, ___, 73

55, 56, ___, 58, ___, ___, ___, ___, 63, ___

___, ___, 75, ___, ___, 78, ___, ___, 81, ___

___, ___, 92, ___, ___, ___, 96, ___, ___, 99

___, ___, ___, ___, 96, ___, 98, ___, 100

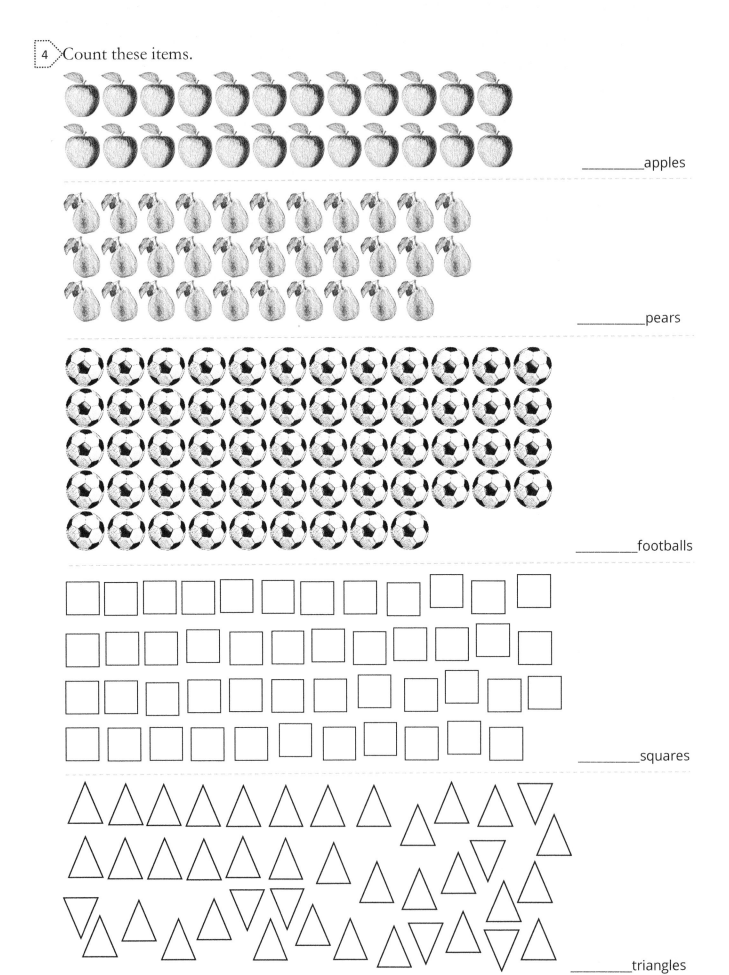

_____apples

_____pears

_____footballs

_____squares

_____triangles

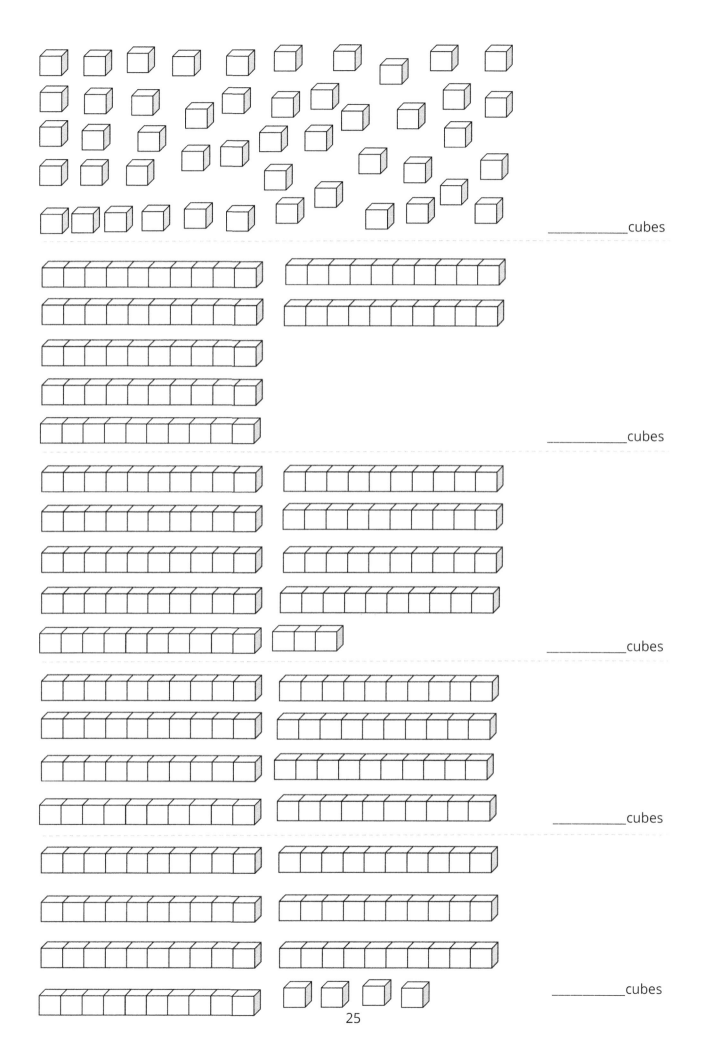

_____ cubes

_____ cubes

_____ cubes

_____ cubes

_____ cubes

Tanya works in a small shop. She counts how many items are left. Is she correct? Circle **Yes** or **No**.

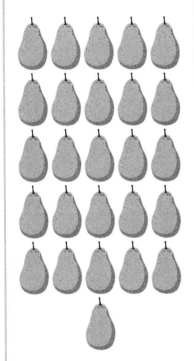

26 pears

Yes / No

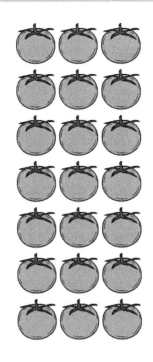

20 tomatoes

Yes / No

28 eggs

Yes / No

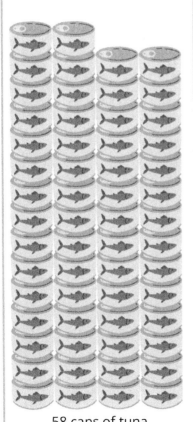

58 cans of tuna

Yes / No

40 pots of noodles

Yes / No

40 tins of soup

Yes / No

6 ▷ Colour in this many squares.

31

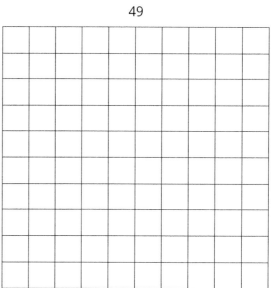

49

60

76

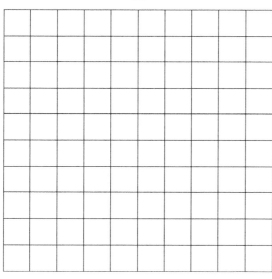

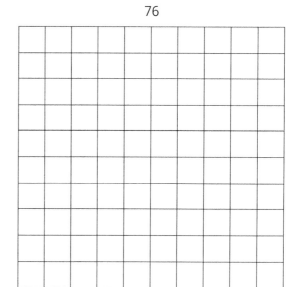

80

50

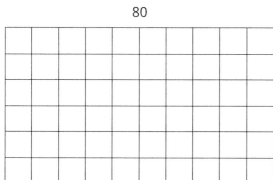

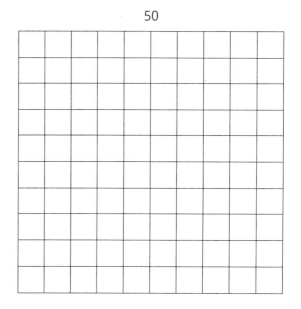

Look at these numbers. What do you notice?

100	99	98	97	96	95	94	93	92	91
90	89	88	87	86	85	84	83	82	81
80	79	78	77	76	75	74	73	72	71
70	69	68	67	66	65	64	63	62	61
60	59	58	57	56	55	54	53	52	51
50	49	48	47	46	45	44	43	42	41
40	39	38	37	36	35	34	33	32	31
30	29	28	27	26	25	24	23	22	21
20	19	18	17	16	15	14	13	12	11
10	9	8	7	6	5	4	3	2	1

The numbers get smaller as you count.

7 > Fill in the grid.

100									91
10									1

8 > Fill the gaps.

30		28		26		24		22	
	32		30		28		26		
		48	47		45			42	
		54				50			47
		71			68		65		
80									71
				96					91
90									81

28

9 Rishi is giving these tins of food to a food bank.

How many tins of food is he giving to the food bank? _____

10 Ken works in a bookstore. He is counting how many books there are in one section of the bookstore.

How many books are there in this section?

_____

11 Jess is counting backwards. She says 33 comes after 32. Is she correct? Why?

_____

12 What is wrong with this number pattern?   51, 49, 48, 47

_____

13 a) How many steps to get from 46 to 42 when counting backwards? _____

b) What number comes after 89? _____

c) Write a number that is between 79 and 82. _____

14 > Dan thinks he has no more than 25 files on his desktop.

Is he correct? Explain your answer.

_____

Progress check

1 > Sidra has some apples and some pears. How many apples and pears does she have?

_____

2 > Jane needs 26 cubes to build a shape. Does she have enough cubes?

_____

3 > Fill the gaps in this pattern: 43, 44, 45, ___, 47, ___, ___, 50

4 > Fill the gaps in this pattern: ___, ___, 72, 73, 74, 75

5 > Put these numbers in order, starting with the largest.

13		25		86	
	16		52		10

_____

6 > Jane completes a number pattern, like this: 78, 79, 81. Is she correct?

_____

Count in twos up to 100

This is how we count in twos.

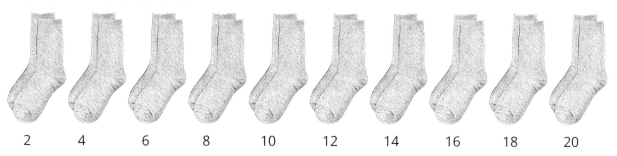

| 2 | 4 | 6 | 8 | 10 | 12 | 14 | 16 | 18 | 20 |

1 Fill the gaps.

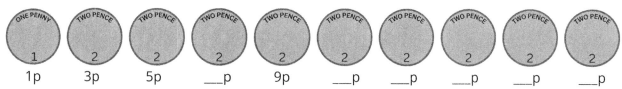

1p   3p   5p   ___p   9p   ___p   ___p   ___p   ___p   ___p

2 Fill the gaps.

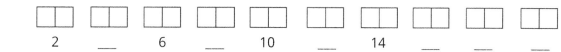

0   2   ___   6   ___   10   ___   14   ___   ___   ___

3 Michaela needs £24 to pay for a bag. This is how much money she has in her purse.

How many more £2 coins does she need?

_____

4 Complete this number pattern by counting in twos.

		24		28		32		36	
	forty two			forty eight					
	63	65		69		73		77	
	eighty five					ninety three		ninety seven	

5 Fill the gaps.

12, 14, ___, 18, ___, 22, ___   65, ___, ___, ___, 73, ___   88, ___, ___, 94, ___, ___

30, ___, 34, 36, ___, ___   72, ___, ___, 78, ___   ___, ___, 44, 46, ___, ___

Progress check

1 How many shoes are there?

_____

2 The tables in a classroom look like this. Two students can sit by each table.

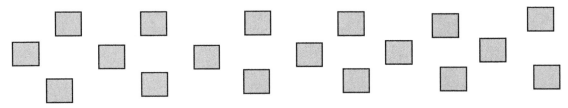

How many students can sit in the classroom?

_____

3 Fill in the gaps in the pattern: 52, 54, 56, ___, 60, ___, ___, 66

4 Fill in the gaps in the pattern: ___, ___, 34, 36, 38, 40

5 A number pattern starts like this: 1, 3, 5, 7 ... and goes up to 31. Will number 21 be in this pattern?

_____

6 Suki completes a number pattern, like this: 43, 45, 46, 48 . Is she correct?

_____

7 Fill in the gaps, counting in ones, twos and backwards.

30, 31, ___, 33, ___, 35, ___   100, 99, ___, 97, ___, ___, ___   42, ___, 46, ___, ___, ___

50, ___, 54, ___, ___, 60   75, ___, ___, 81, 83, ___   68, ___, ___, 74, ___, ___

___, ___, 84, 82, ___, 78   72, 71, ___, ___, ___, ___, ___

Counting in tens, twenties and fives, up to 100

Counting in tens up to 100

This is how we count in tens.

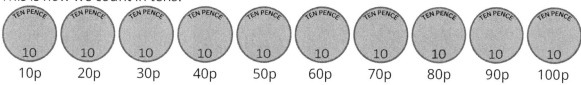

10p 20p 30p 40p 50p 60p 70p 80p 90p 100p

1 ▷ Fill the gaps.

a)

10 ___ 30 ___ 50 ___ ___

b)

£10 £20 ___ ___ ___

Counting in 20s up to 100

This is how we count in twenties.

20p 40p 60p 80p 100p

2 ▷ Fill the gaps.

a)

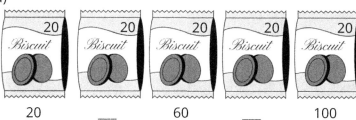

20 ___ 60 ___ 100

b)

£20 ___ £60 ___ ___

Counting in fives up to 100

This is how we count in fives.

5p 10p 15p 20p 25p 30p 35p 40p 45p 50p 55p 60p

3 Fill the gaps.

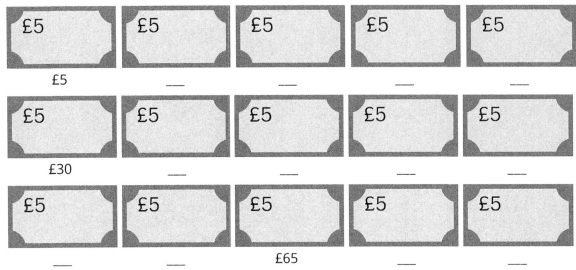

£5 £5 £5 £5 £5
£5 ___ ___ ___ ___

£5 £5 £5 £5 £5
£30 ___ ___ ___ ___

£5 £5 £5 £5 £5
___ ___ £65 ___ ___

4 Fill the gaps.

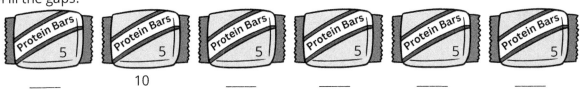

___ 10 ___ ___ ___ ___

5 Fill the gaps.

5, 10, 15, ___, 25, ___, 35   17, 27, 37, ___, ___, ___   20, ___, ___, ___, 100   5, 15, 25, ___, 45, ___

20, ___, 30, 35, 40, ___, 50   43, ___, 63, ___, ___, 93   32, 42, ___, ___, ___   39, 49, ___, ___, 79

65, ___, ___, 80, 85, ___   60, ___, ___, ___, 100   0, 20, 40, ___, 80, ___   95, 75, 55, ___, ___

6 Stef is giving change to a customer. She thinks she has given £1 change.

10 10 20 20 20

Is Stef correct?

_____

7 Jay is counting the minutes in one hour: **5, 10, 15, 20, 30, 35, 40, 45, 50, 55, 60**
What mistake did he make?_____

Progress check

1. Lisa is playing a game online. She has scored 43 points so far. She is now earning 10 points. How many points does she have now?

_____

2. Nita checks her bank balance and it is £67. She withdraws £20. What is the new balance?

_____

3.
a) Ali is a teacher. In his class, there are 28 students. He is buying one pen for each student.

Will three packs be enough?

_____

b) There are five cookies in one bag.

Julie thinks there are 35 cookies in seven bags. Is Julie correct?

_____

c) One of these boxes weighs 10kg. How many boxes will weigh 100kg in total?

_____

d) A tin of chicken soup costs 20p.

How many tins can be bought with 45p?

_____

e) One lollipop costs 20p. How many can you buy with 70p?

_____

f) Drew is withdrawing money from the cash machine. She gets ten £5 notes. How much has she withdrawn?

£5

_____

g) Martin is a baker. He bakes 5 trays of cupcakes every day. Each tray has 20 cupcakes on it.

How many cupcakes does Martin bake daily?

_____

h) A school is organising a field trip and has four buses. Each bus can carry 20 students.

How many students can go on the field trip using these buses?

_____

i) Sony writes this number pattern:

45, 54, 64, 74, 84

What is wrong with the pattern?

_____

j) Van writes this number pattern:

72, 52, 42, 32, 22

What is wrong with the pattern?

_____

4. Siobhan says 'Counting in 10s is easy as numbers end in 0'. Is Siobhan correct?

_____

5. Ayla says 'Counting in 5s is also easy as numbers end in 0 or 5'. Is Ayla correct?

_____

Recognise and sequence odd and even numbers up to 100

Door numbers, socks, shoes or gloves can be odd or even.

Houses on one side of the road have odd numbers. For example: 13, 15, 17, 19.
Houses on the other side of the road have even numbers. For example: 14, 16, 18, 20.

This is an odd sock.

This is a pair of socks (2 is even)

Odd numbers go like this:

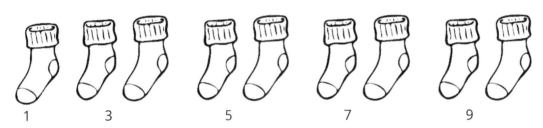

| 1 | 3 | 5 | 7 | 9 |

Even numbers go like this:

| 2 | 4 | 6 | 8 | 10 |

1 ▷ Fill the gaps.

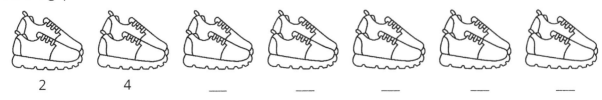

2   4   ___   ___   ___   ___   ___

Fill the gaps.

a)

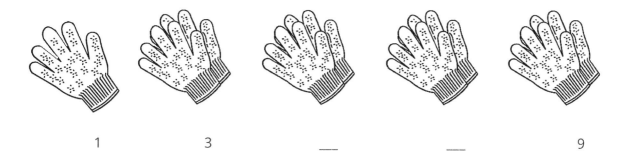

| 1 | 3 | __ | __ | 9 |

b)

| 65 | __ | 69 | __ |

3 Write the missing even numbers.

1		3		5		7		9	
11		13		15		17		19	
21		23		25		27		29	
31		33		35		37		39	
41		43		45		47		49	
51		53		55		57		59	
61		63		65		67		69	
71		73		75		77		79	
81		83		85		87		89	
91		93		95		97		99	

What do you notice about even numbers?

Even numbers end in 0, 2, 4, 6, 8.

4 Write the missing odd numbers.

	2		4		6		8		10
	12		14		16		18		20
	22		24		26		28		30
	32		34		36		38		40
	42		44		46		48		50
	52		54		56		58		60
	62		64		66		68		70
	72		74		76		78		80
	82		84		86		88		90
	92		94		96		98		100

What do you notice about odd numbers?

Odd numbers end in 1, 3, 5, 7, 9.

5 a) Write an odd number that is greater than 5.

_____

b) Write an even number that is smaller than 13.

_____

6 Match these numbers with the right word.

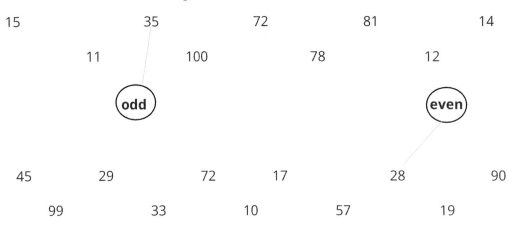

15   35   72   81   14

     11   100   78   12

          (odd)   (even)

45   29   72   17   28   90

   99   33   10   57   19

7 The house numbers on one side of the road go like this: **35, 37, 39, 41, 43 ...**
Will 54 be on the same side of the road? _____

8 A building has 30 apartments with door numbers from 1 to 30. The even-numbered apartments are on the right side of the building, and the odd-numbered apartments are on the left side. Sana thinks apartment 23 will be located on the right of the building as number 2 is even. Is she correct?

_____

9 Is number **ninety nine** odd or even?

_____

10 Fill the gaps.

7 + 5 = ___	15 + 9 = ___	23 + 17 = ___	odd	+ odd	=	even
6 + 8 = ___	10 + 14 = ___	26 + 26 = ___	even	+ even	=	
9 + 12 = ___	11 + 6 = ___	21 + 34 = ___	odd	+ even	=	
6 + 7 = ___	12 + 7 = ___	36 + 13 = ___	even	+ odd	=	

11 Jack is training for a marathon and increases his daily run by 2 kilometers each day. On Monday, he runs 6 kilometers. How many kilometers will he run on Friday?

_____

12 A train has seats numbered from 1 to 40. The even-numbered seats are by the window. Sam is sitting in seat number 38. Is she sitting by the window? Why?

_____

Progress check

1 Are these numbers odd or even? Put them in the circle they belong: **8, 11, 25, 50, 56, 77, 81, 100**

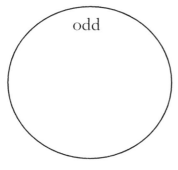
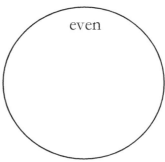

odd

even

2 Becky is counting her socks. Continue counting: 22, 24, 26, ___, ___, ___

3 Add the missing numbers in this pattern: ___, 39, 41, 43, ___

4 Ola says: 'After each even number, comes an odd number'. Is she right? Explain.

_____

5 Nick says: 'I just look at the last digit of the number to decide if it is odd or even. 23 is odd because 3 is odd. 56 is even because 6 is even.' Is Nick correct?

_____

Add and subtract two-digit numbers

In everyday life, we add and subtract, to work out:
- ➤ the cost of items we are buying and the change we will g
- ➤ the number of hours spent studying in a week
- ➤ the cost of bills or subscriptions per year
- ➤ the distance between two places
- ➤ the scores in a game
- ➤ the cost of organizing an event
- ➤ the amount of paint you need to paint the walls
- ➤ the amount for each ingredient when cooking for many
- ➤ the savings made over a year

Add two-digit numbers

The number line method of addition

To work out 13 + 25, we do: 13 + 10 = 23;   23 + 10 = 33;   33 + 5 = 38

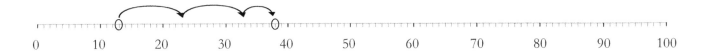

To work out 46 + 32, we do: 46 + 10 = 56;   56 + 10 = 66;   66 + 10 = 76;   76 + 2 = 78

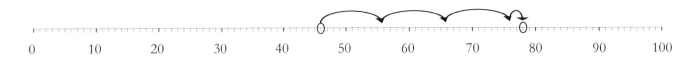

1 Use the number line to add.

63 + 31 =

79 + 21 =

57 + 11 =

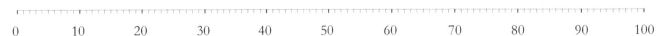

46 + 22 =

0   10   20   30   40   50   60   70   80   90   100

76 + 23 =

0   10   20   30   40   50   60   70   80   90   100

48 + 34 =

0   10   20   30   40   50   60   70   80   90   100

64 + 25 =

0   10   20   30   40   50   60   70   80   90   100

63 + 8 =

0   10   20   30   40   50   60   70   80   90   100

57 + 28 =

0   10   20   30   40   50   60   70   80   90   100

52 + 41 =

0   10   20   30   40   50   60   70   80   90   100

33 + 37 =

0   10   20   30   40   50   60   70   80   90   100

51 + 36 =

0   10   20   30   40   50   60   70   80   90   100

When adding two big numbers:

Example: 64 + 52

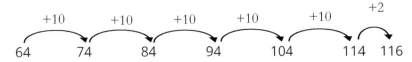

Example: 75 + 47

Example: 93 + 64

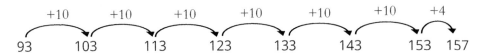

2 Add these numbers.

84 + 25 =
57 + 53 =
92 + 46 =
89 + 42 =
73 + 67 =
63 + 94 =
99 + 99 =

When adding numbers that are very close to 100, such as 99 and 56, you can borrow 1 from 56 to give to 99, to make it easy to add: 100 + 55 = 155

The part-whole method of addition

This is another method you can use to add.

35 + 23	**43 + 48**
We split 35 into 30 and 5. We split 23 into 20 and 3.	We split 43 into 40 and 3. We split 48 into 40 and 8.

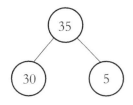 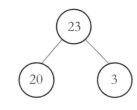 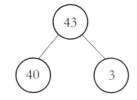 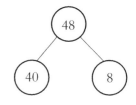

Now we add the tens: 30 + 20 = 50

And the ones: 5 + 3 = 8

Altogether: 50 + 8 = 58

Now we add the tens: 40 + 40 = 80

And the ones: 3 + 8 = 11

Altogether: 80 + 11 = 91

3 ▷ Work out.

a) 27 + 12 =

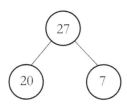

b) 44 + 20 =

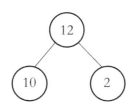

c) 55 + 29 =

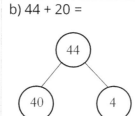

d) 35 + 27 =

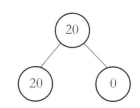

e) 64 + 32 =

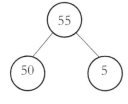

f) 48 + 26 =

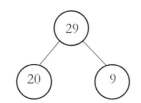

a) 61 + 24 =

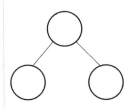 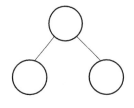

b) 86 + 11 =

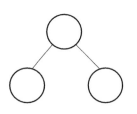

c) 73 + 19 =

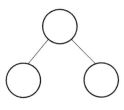 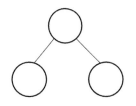

d) 24 + 25 =

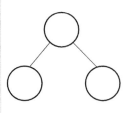 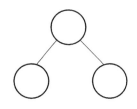

e) 63 + 33 =

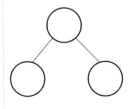 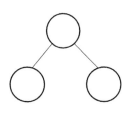

f) 75 + 26 =

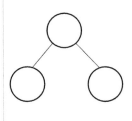 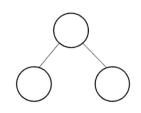

g) 70 + 27 =

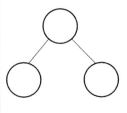 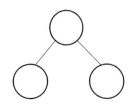

h) 62 + 23 =

 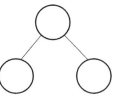 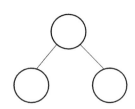

i) 27 + 32 =

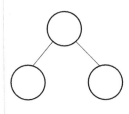 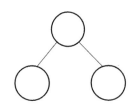

j) 44 + 59 =

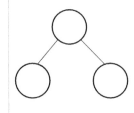 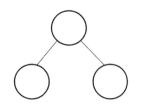

The column method of addition

Example 1

Blocks of ten	Ones
1	4
+	
2	4
3	8

Example 2

Blocks of ten	Ones
1	
3	5
+	
2	5
6	0

Blocks of ten	Ones

Blocks of ten	Ones

45

Here are some more examples.

3 4 + 6 5 ——— 9 9	6 7 + 2 1 ——— 8 8	3 5 + 4 1 ——— 7 6	¹2 4 + 3 6 ——— 6 0

4 + 6 = 10 so we put 0 under the units and 1 is carried over to the tens

You align <u>units</u> under the <u>units</u>, <u>tens</u> under the <u>tens</u>.

5 ⟩ Fill the gaps.

1 3 + 1 6 ———	1 2 + 2 5 ———	4 5 + 3 4 ———	1 0 + 6 7 ———	3 3 + 5 7 ———	1 3 + 4 6 ———	5 4 + 2 5 ———
3 8 + 4 1 ———	1 6 + 3 2 ———	1 5 + 7 3 ———	5 4 + 2 6 ———	2 2 + 6 7 ———	5 1 + 3 8 ———	2 4 + 3 4 ———
6 8 + 1 1 ———	1 0 + 5 8 ———	3 4 + 6 5 ———	4 2 + 4 7 ———	6 5 + 2 4 ———	1 0 + 7 9 ———	5 3 + 3 3 ———
2 5 + 5 5 ———	1 1 + 5 1 ———	6 2 + 3 4 ———	6 0 + 3 0 ———	5 4 + 2 2 ———	6 6 + 3 ———	7 1 + 2 6 ———
6 2 + 2 5 ———	5 3 + 1 5 ———	2 6 + 4 3 ———	4 1 + ___ ——— 5 8	3 5 + ___ ——— 6 9	2 3 + ___ ——— 8 7	4 4 + ___ ——— 6 0

46

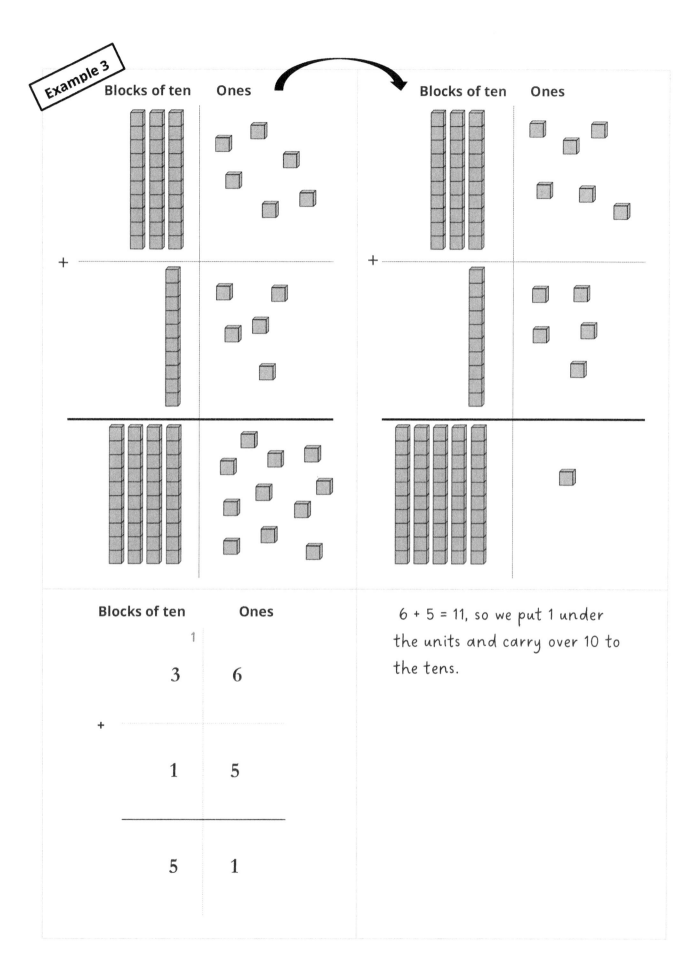

Example 3

Blocks of ten	Ones
1	
3	6
+	
1	5
5	1

6 + 5 = 11, so we put 1 under the units and carry over 10 to the tens.

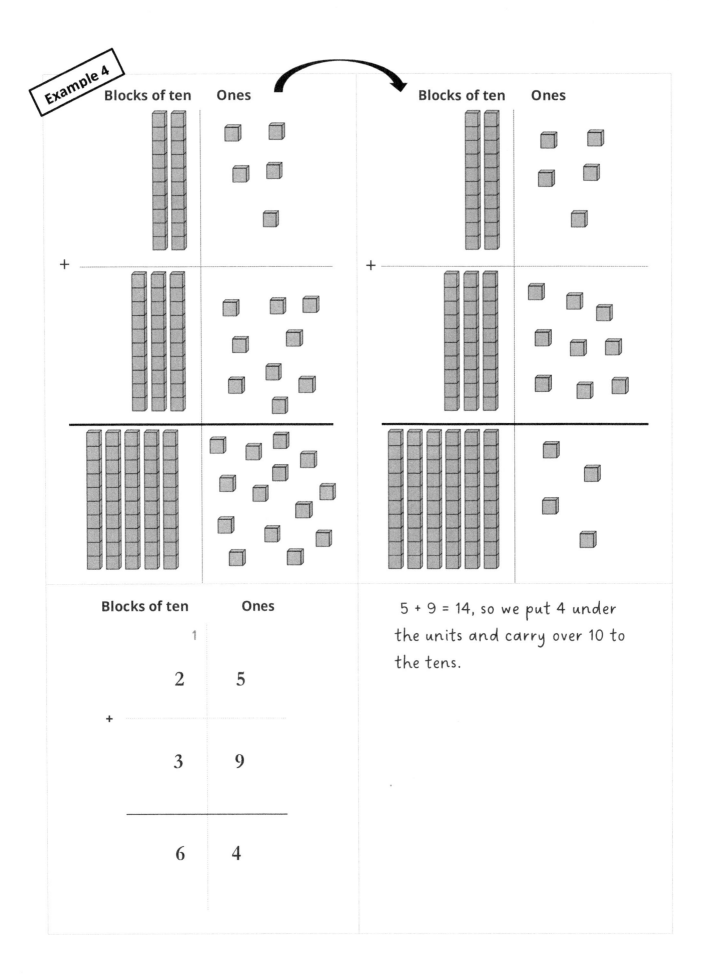

Example 4

Blocks of ten	Ones
1	
2	5
+	
3	9
———	———
6	4

5 + 9 = 14, so we put 4 under the units and carry over 10 to the tens.

Example 5

Hundreds	Tens	Ones

	Hundreds	Tens	Ones
+			

Hundreds	Tens	Ones
1		1
	7	6
+		
	5	8
1	3	4

As 6 + 8 = 14, we carry 10 over to the tens column and put 4 in the ones column.

As 7 + 5 + 1 = 13, we carry 10 over to the hundreds column and put 3 in the tens column.

Example 6

Hundreds	Tens	Ones

+

Hundreds	Tens	Ones
1	1	
	8	8
+		
	8	4
1	7	2

As 8 + 4 = 12, we carry 10 over to the tens column and put 2 in the ones column.

As 8 + 8 + 1 = 17, we carry 10 over to the hundreds column and put 7 in the tens column.

Here are some more examples.

	1				1		1				1		1
	4	5			7	2				8	8		
+				+					+				
	4	7			9	9				7	5		
	9	2		1	7	1			1	6	3		

6 Fill the gaps.

+ 91 67	+ 24 85	+ 56 84	+ 90 87	+ 93 73	+ 13 96	+ 14 57
+ 48 81	+ 76 27	+ 15 72	+ 84 26	+ 26 77	+ 91 38	+ 64 74
+ 41 48	+ 70 58	+ 54 82	+ 72 57	+ 65 74	+ 92 19	+ 53 83
+ 95 25	+ 31 75	+ 62 76	+ 59 10	+ 14 27	+ 86 57	+ 58 96
+ 42 85	+ 73 35	+ 16 73	+ 78 ___ / 89	+ 47 ___ / 78	+ 68 ___ / 137	+ 80 ___ / 175

You can use whichever method you like to subtract. It is good practice to know at least two methods as it helps with deeper understanding and in case you forget one under exam conditions.

Add these numbers.

14 + 5 = ____	23 + 8 = ____	16 + 27 = ____	59 + 14 = ____
5 + 14 = ____	8 + 23 = ____	27 + 16 = ____	14 + 59 = ____

What do you notice?

Order doesn't matter when adding.

7 Sylvia read 26 pages of a book in the morning and 38 pages in the afternoon. How many pages has she read in total?

_____

8 Nadia spent £76 on clothing and £39 on food. How much did she spend in total?

_____

9 Dan's phone has 43GB free storage space. He also has a memory card on the phone, with 64GB capacity. How much free storage does Dan's phone have?

_____

10 Atif is going to visit a friend. It takes 25 minutes to go to his friend's house. He will stay for 60 minutes and then return home. Atif thinks the whole journey will take 120 minutes. Is he correct?

_____

11 Katheryn says: 'When adding 0 to a number, the number stays the same'. Is Katheryn correct?

_____

12 Sarah goes shopping and buys a shirt for £35 and a pair of shoes for £45. How much money did she spend in total?

_____

13 At a charity event, 72 people attend in the morning and 95 people attend in the afternoon. How many people attended the event in total?

_____

Progress check

1. You buy two reusable carrier bags to put your shopping in, like below.

69p   99p

How much do both bags cost? _____p

2. How many cubes are there altogether? Show your working.

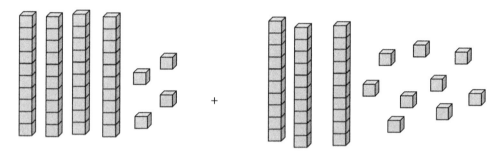

_____

3. Fill in the gaps below:

| 27 + 15 = ___ | 12 + ___ = 35 | ___ + 9 = 79 |
| 44 + 26 = ___ | 58 + ___ = 66 | ___ + 14 = 93 |

4. Naila writes these maths sentences: 24 + 4 = 4 + 24
                                                        0 + 35 = 0

5. Do you agree with Naila? Explain your answer.

_____

6. Find another two numbers you can add which give the same total as 25 + 46

_____

7. In a gym, 43 people are using the treadmills and 36 people are using the exercise bikes. How many people are exercising in total?

_____

Subtract two-digit numbers

To work out 25 - 13, we do: 25 - 10 = 15;   15 - 3 = 12

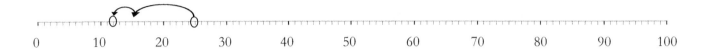

To work out 46 - 32, we do: 46 - 10 = 36;   36 - 10 = 26;   26 - 10 = 16;   16 - 2 = 14

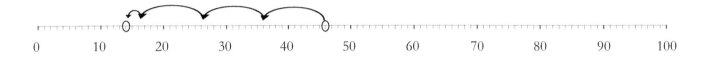

1 Use the number line to subtract.

63 - 31 =

79 - 21 =

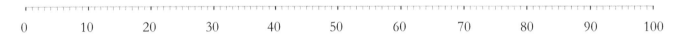

57 - 11 =

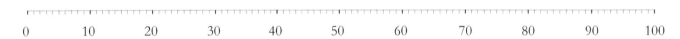

46 - 22 =

76 - 23 =

48 - 34 =

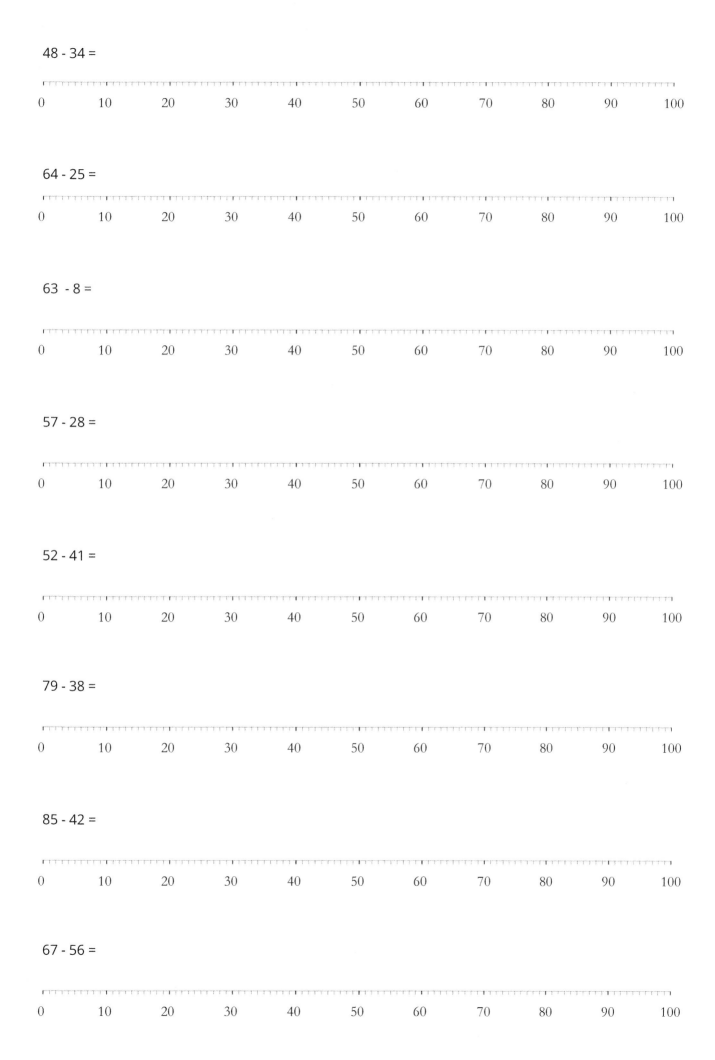

0   10   20   30   40   50   60   70   80   90   100

64 - 25 =

0   10   20   30   40   50   60   70   80   90   100

63 - 8 =

0   10   20   30   40   50   60   70   80   90   100

57 - 28 =

0   10   20   30   40   50   60   70   80   90   100

52 - 41 =

0   10   20   30   40   50   60   70   80   90   100

79 - 38 =

0   10   20   30   40   50   60   70   80   90   100

85 - 42 =

0   10   20   30   40   50   60   70   80   90   100

67 - 56 =

0   10   20   30   40   50   60   70   80   90   100

The part-whole method of subtraction

This is another method you can use to subtract.

35 - 23	**78 - 44**
We split 35 into 30 and 5.	We split 78 into 70 and 8.
We split 23 into 20 and 3.	We split 44 into 40 and 4.

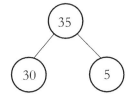 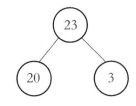 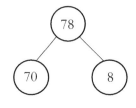 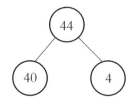

Now we subtract the tens: 30 - 20 = 10

And the ones: 5 - 3 = 2

Altogether: 10 + 2 = 12

Now we subtract the tens: 70 - 40 = 30

And the ones: 8 - 4 = 4

Altogether: 30 + 4 = 34

2 Subtract these numbers.

a) 47 - 31 =

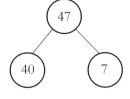

b) 68 - 45 =

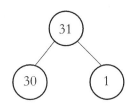

c) 65 - 35 =

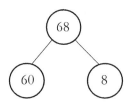

d) 89 - 63 =

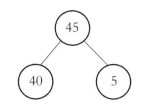

e) 97 – 42 =

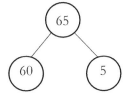

f) 44 - 33 =

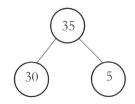

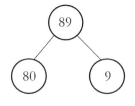

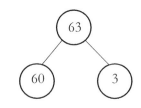

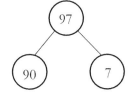

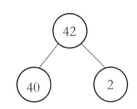

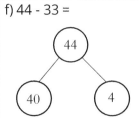

a) 35 – 23 =

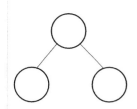 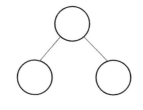

b) 47 – 16 =

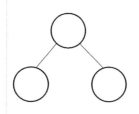 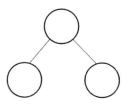

c) 97 – 42 =

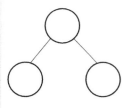 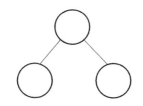

d) 36 – 26 =

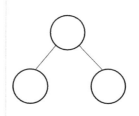 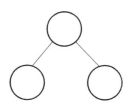

e) 68 – 64 =

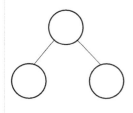 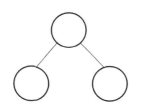

f) 35 – 13 =

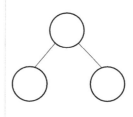 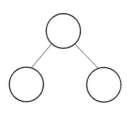

g) 59 – 41 =

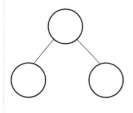 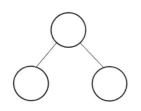

h) 77 – 40 =

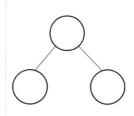 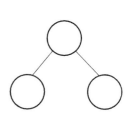

i) 37 – 26 =

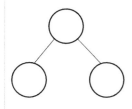 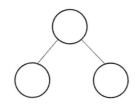

j) 56 – 44 =

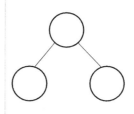 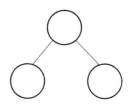

The column method of subtraction

Example 1

Blocks of ten	Ones
4	9
-	
2	4
2	5

Example 2

Blocks of ten	Ones
	1
6	5
-	
3	5
3	0

Blocks of ten	Ones

Blocks of ten	Ones

58

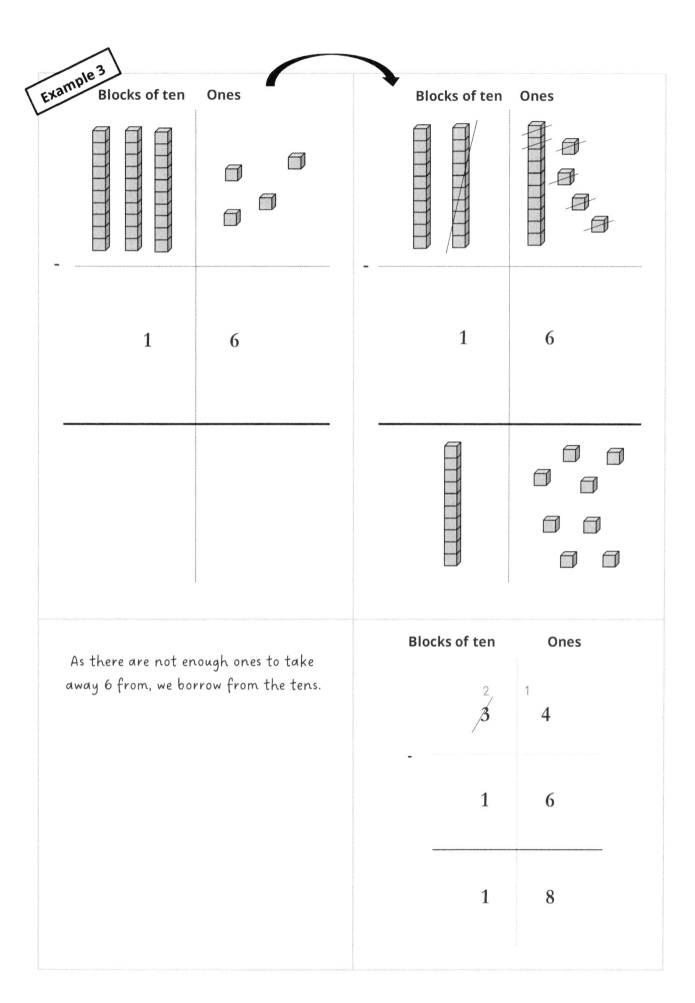

Example 3

Blocks of ten	Ones

1	6

Blocks of ten	Ones

1	6

As there are not enough ones to take away 6 from, we borrow from the tens.

Blocks of ten	Ones
2	1
3	4
-	
1	6
1	8

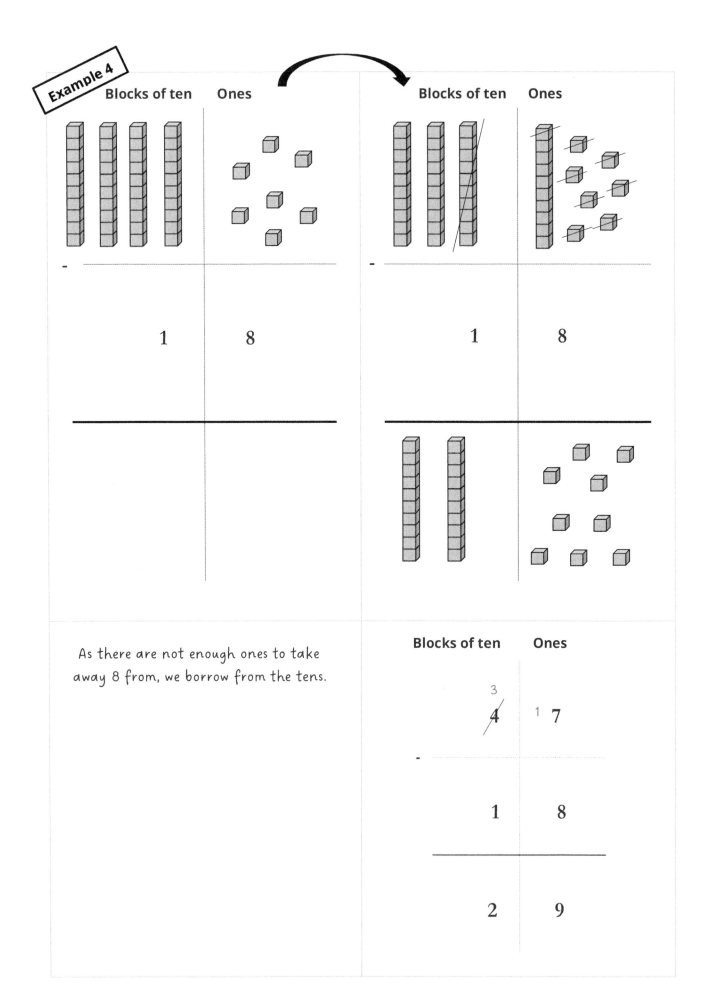

Example 4

| Blocks of ten | Ones | | Blocks of ten | Ones |

1   8   1   8

As there are not enough ones to take away 8 from, we borrow from the tens.

Blocks of ten	Ones
³ 4̸	¹ 7
− 1	8
2	9

60

Here are some more examples.

$\overset{4}{\cancel{5}}$ $\overset{1}{4}$	$\overset{6}{\cancel{7}}$ $\overset{1}{2}$	$\overset{8}{\cancel{9}}$ $\overset{1}{8}$	$\overset{3}{\cancel{4}}$ $\overset{1}{5}$
− 3 8	− 3 7	− 4 7	− 1 6
1 6	3 5	2 1	2 9

> You align units under the units, tens under the tens.

4 Fill the gaps.

4 1 − 7	6 2 − 4 5	7 5 − 3 4	8 0 − 4 7	7 3 − 3 7	5 3 − 2 6	9 4 − 6 6
− 6 8 4 1	6 6 − 6 2	4 5 − 3 3	8 4 − 4 6	9 2 − 5 7	6 5 − 2 9	6 4 − 2 4
4 1 − 2 8	5 0 − 3 8	6 4 − 4 2	6 2 − 3 7	7 5 − 5 4	8 0 − 6 9	8 3 − 6 3
3 5 − 2 5	4 1 − 2 1	4 2 − 2 2	6 0 − 1 0	4 4 − 2 7	9 6 − 6 7	7 1 − 4 6
7 2 − 3 5	6 3 − 2 5	4 6 − 3 3	7 8 − 1 1	5 5 − 1 2	5 3 − 7	6 0 − 5

61

Use a calculator to subtract these numbers.

6 – 4 = ___ and 4 – 6 = ____   10 – 3 = ___ and 3 – 10 = ____

20 – 14 = ____ and 14 – 20 = ____   54 – 14 = ____ and 14 – 54 = ____

What do you notice?

Order matters when subtracting.
4 - 3 = 1   3 - 4 = -1

At this level you do:
greater number - smaller number

5 > Sylvia bought 43 books last year. She read 17 of them. How many books has she not read yet?

_____

6 > a) Veronica exercised for 36 minutes on Monday. She exercised for 20 minutes on Wednesday.
How many more minutes did she do on Wednesday than on Monday?

_____

b) How can Veronica check her answer?

_____

Language is important!
Subtract 7 **from** 9:
Example: 9 – 7 = 2

7 > Donna has £53. She spends £15 on food.
Donna wants to work out how money much she has left: 53 – 15 = 38
Is Donna correct?

_____

8 > Hana has 24 eggs in the fridge. She uses four eggs to make a cake.
Hana wants to work out how many eggs are left: 4 - 24 = 20 Is Hana correct?

_____

9 > Mike has 68 litres of petrol in his car. He fills up an additional 24 litres. To work out how many litres
of petrol he has now, he calculates: 68 – 24 = 44   Is Mike correct?

_____

10 > Nicole says: 'When subtracting 0 from a number, the number stays the same'. Is Nicole correct?

_____

The link between addition and subtraction

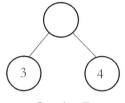

3 + 4 = 7

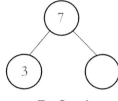

7 – 3 = 4

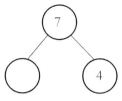

7 – 4 = 3

What do you notice?

3 + ___ = 7 is the same as 7 – 3

___ + 4 = 7 is the same as 7 – 4

Addition ⟷ Subtraction
Addition is the opposite of subtraction.
Subtraction is the opposite of addition.

11. Fill the gaps. The first one has been done for you.

6 + ___ = 13 is the same as 13 – 7   ___ + 7 = 13 is the same as 13 – 7

9 + ___ = 14 is the same as _____   ___ + 5 = 14 is the same as _____

5 + ___ = 12 is the same as _____   ___ + 7 = 12 is the same as _____

8 + ___ = 19 is the same as _____   ___ + 11 = 19 is the same as _____

12. Fill the gaps.

27 take away 8 is written as 27 – 8   Take away 14 **from** 24 is written as 24 – 14

33 take away 9 is written as 33 – 9   Take away 36 from 45 is written as 45 – 16

59 take away 28 is written as _____   Take away 25 from 37 is written as _____

60 take away 11 is written as _____   Take away 9 from 44 is written as _____

46 take away 34 is written as _____   Take away 11 from 89 is written as _____

Checking answers

Example: Naila has 26 blue balloons and 13 red balloons. How many balloons does Naila have in total? 26 + 13 = 39 **To check the answer:** 39 – 13 = 26 or 39 – 26 = 13

Example: Dan has planted 39 flowers in the garden. He then plants another 17. How many flowers has Dan planted altogether? 39 + 17 = 56 **To check:** 56 – 17 = 39 or 56 – 39 = 17

Example: Jackie needs to buy 28 new cups. She buys 6. How many more does she need to buy? 28 – 6 = 22 **To check:** 22 + 6 = 28 or 6 + 22 = 28

Example: There are 27 apples in the fridge. Tom takes 6. How many apples are left? 27 – 6 = 21 **To check:** 21 + 6 = 27 or 6 + 21 = 27

13. Ben spent 15 minutes reading and 5 minutes on a break. How many minutes has Ben spent altogether?

_____

Check your answer:

_____

14. Sukhdev has 19 pens. He gives 12 to his students. How many pens does Sukhdev have now?

_____

Check your answer:

_____

15. George has £70 in his wallet. He buys lunch for £15. How much money does George have left?

_____

Check your answer:

_____

16. A train has a capacity of 80 passengers. Currently, 57 passengers are on board. How many more passengers can the train accommodate?

_____

Check your answer:

_____

17. Ben reads 15 Pages of a book on Monday and 25 Pages on Tuesday. How many Pages has he read in total?

_____

Check your answer:

_____

18. Mary bakes 24 cookies and gives 10 away to her friends. How many cookies does Mary have left?

_____

Check your answer:

_____

19. Kevin runs 5 miles on Monday and 8 miles on Wednesday. How many miles does Kevin run in total?

_____

Check your answer:

_____

Difference means **taking away**.
Example: The difference between 7 and 9 is 2.

20 a) What is the difference between 20 and 5?

_____

b) Work out the difference between 36 and 100.

_____

c) What is the difference between 72 and 54?

_____

d) Work out the difference between 45 and 90.

_____

21 a) Hollie had 36 unread emails when she started work. She now has this many unread emails.

How many emails did she read?

_____

b) Kim has ordered some items online. They will be delivered in 14 days. Kim checks the calendar and this is the date.

On which date will the items be delivered?

_____

c) Zen is waiting at the bus stop. He is going to the city centre.
The bus will be 9 minutes late. It takes 27 minutes to get to the city centre by bus. How long will it take altogether to get to the city centre?

_____

d) Roy's phone bill is £25 per month.
From next month, the bill will go up by £6.

How much will the new bill be?

_____

e) This is how many tablets Gert takes in a day:

Two in the morning
Three at lunch
Two in the evening

How many tablets does Gert take over three days?

_____

f) Tara is going to a new shop. She checks on Google and it takes 23 minutes to walk to the shop.

As Tara uses a wheelchair, she adds five minutes to the journey. How long will it take Tara to go to the shop?

_____

g) Jack has a sister called Suki. Jack is 46 years old. Suki is fifteen years older.

How old is Suki?

_____

h) Amanda exercised for 27 minutes in the morning and 36 minutes in the afternoon. How many minutes did Amanda exercise for in total?

_____

i) During a cultural festival, 35 participants are wearing traditional outfits and 25 are wearing casual clothes.

How many participants are there in total?

_____

j) Joshua's phone has a 64GB memory capacity. He adds memory card with 64GB to the phone.
How many GB does the phone have, including the memory card?

_____

22 Fill the gaps with numbers. The first one has been done for you.

18	+	6	=	24
	+		=	32
	+		=	41
33	=		+	
27	=		+	

30	-	7	=	23
	-		=	15
	-		=	6
10	=		-	
12	=		-	

23 Fill the gaps. The first one has been done for you.

28	+	16	=	44
	+		=	44
	+		=	44
44	=		+	
44	=		+	

50	-	37	=	13
	-		=	13
	-		=	13
13	=		-	
13	=		-	

Subtract these numbers.

$4 - 4 =$ ____ $\qquad$ $13 - 13 =$ ____ $\qquad$ $16 - 16 =$ ____ $\qquad$ $9 - 9 =$ ____

$15 - 15 =$ ____ $\qquad$ $10 - 10 =$ ____ $\qquad$ $17 - 17 =$ ____ $\qquad$ $14 - 14 =$ ____

What do you notice?

When you subtract the number itself, you get 0.
$12 - 12 = \mathbf{0}$ $\qquad$ $13 - 13 = \mathbf{0}$

24 Work out:

$25 - 25 =$	$18 - 18 =$	$56 - 56 =$	$12 - 12 =$	$20 - 20 =$	$0 - 0 =$

25 Fill the gaps.

+
6	8
2	
9	5

+
	8
3	5
6	

+
	4
4	
8	2

+
2	3
6	1

26 Fill the gaps.

-	6	8
	2	
	4	5

-		8
	3	
	4	9

-		4
	4	
	1	7

-	7	3
	6	9

27 Ayla is adding 62 and 18. This is how she has lined the numbers up. What has she done wrong?

_____

+		6	2
	1	8	
	2	4	2

Progress check

1 You have 90p in your pocket. You buy a plastic carrier bag to put your shopping in. The bag costs 44p.

How much money do you have left after paying for the bag? _____p

2 Lela needs 24 portions of cake for her guests. She has already made 8. How many more does she need to make?

_____

3 Fill in the gaps.

| 39 - 5 = ____ | 54 - 26 = ____ | 55 - ____ = 12 | 76 - ____ = 8 | ____ - 59 = 10 | ____ - 4 = 81 |

4 Ayla writes these maths sentences:

24 - 4 = 4 - 24

25 - 0 = 25

Do you agree with Ayla? Explain your answer.

_____

5 Find another two numbers you can subtract which have the same difference as 34 and 3.

_____

6 Check these calculations.

8 + 8 = 16   Check: _____   8 + 6 = 14   Check: _____

5 + 12 = 17   Check: _____   9 + 6 = 15   Check: _____

Multiply whole numbers in the range 0x0 to 12x12 (times tables)

We multiply when calculating:

> ➢ the cost of multiple items
> ➢ how long it takes to do a task again and again
> ➢ pay per week, given number of hours worked
> ➢ how much you will pay per month or year for bills
> ➢ how much of each ingredient you need when cooking
> ➢ how much paint you may need to paint walls

The chocolate bar has 4 rows with 6 squares in each row.

To work out the total number of squares, we can do: 6+ 6 + 6 + 6 which is the same as: 4 lots of 6 ⟹ 4 x 6 = 24

Example:	Example:
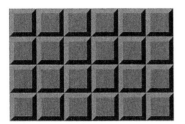	
There are four yogurt pots is one pack. In three packs, there will be: 4 + 4 + 4 or 3 x 4 = 12	A tin of soup costs £2. Six tins of soup will cost: 2 + 2 + 2 + 2 + 2 + 2 or 6 x 2 = £12

These are the multiplication facts you need to know.

x	0	1	2	3	4	5	6	7	8	9	10	11	12
0	0	0	0	0	0	0	0	0	0	0	0	0	0
1	0	1	2	3	4	5	6	7	8	9	10	11	12
2	0	2	4	6	8	10	12	14	16	18	20	22	24
3	0	3	6	9	12	15	18	21	24	27	30	33	36
4	0	4	8	12	16	20	24	28	32	36	40	44	48 ▾
5	0	5	10	15	20	25	30	35	40	45	50	55	60
6	0	6	12	18	24	30	36	42	48	54	60	66	72
7	0	7	14	21	28	35	42	49	56	63	70	77	84
8	0	8	16	24	32	40	48	56	64	72	80	88	96
9	0	9	18	27	36	45	54	63	72	81	90	99	108
10	0	10	20	30	40	50	60	70	80	90	100	110	120
11	0	11	22	33	44	55	66	77	88	99	110	121	132
12	0	12	24	36	48	60	72	84	96	108	120	131	144

4 x 12 = 48

What do you notice? Look at the numbers that are repeated.

Multiplying by 0

When multiplying by 0, the answer is always 0.

0 x 0 = **0**	**0** x 7 = **0**
0 x 1 = **0**	**0** x 8 = **0**
0 x 2 = **0**	**0** x 9 = **0**
0 x 3 = **0**	**0** x 10 = **0**
0 x 4 = **0**	**0** x 11 = **0**
0 x 5 = **0**	**0** x 12 = **0**
0 x 6 = **0**	

It's like planning to go to the shop to buy a number of items but in fact you go 0 times (you don't go). So you bring **nothing** home.
Even 100 x 0 = 0,
165 x 0 = 0

1 You plan to go shopping and buy six items. However, you have no time and don't go to the shop. How many items do you buy?

_____

2 The local food bank is giving food for free to people in need. Andy gets five food items. How much does he pay for these items?

_____

Multiplying by 1

When multiplying by 1, the answer is the number you multiply by 1.

1 x 0 = 0
1 x 1 = 1
1 x 2 = 2
1 x 3 = 3
1 x 4 = 4
1 x 5 = 5
1 x 6 = 6
1 x 7 = 7
1 x 8 = 8
1 x 9 = 9
1 x 10 = 10
1 x 11 = 11
1 x 12 = 12

It's like going **once** to the shop and getting 1 item each time.
1 x 100 = 100;
142 x 1 = 142

Multiplying by 2

When multiplying by 2, the answer is **double** the number you're multiplying.

2 x 0 = 0
2 x 1 = 2
2 x 2 = 4
2 x 3 = 6
2 x 4 = 8
2 x 5 = 10
2 x 6 = 12
2 x 7 = 14
2 x 8 = 16
2 x 9 = 18
2 x 10 = 20
2 x 11 = 22
2 x 12 = 24

To work out 2 x 12, just do 12 + 12 so 2 lots of 12.

3 You go to the shop one time and buy 10 items. How many items do you bring home?

_____

4 Lana is buying eight pairs of socks. One pair cost £1. How much will eight pairs cost?

_____

5. Janey is giving two sweets to each of her children. Janey has five children. How many sweets does Janey give to her children?

_____

6. Naz bought two rolls of wrapping paper. Each roll is 7 metres long. How long will the two rolls be altogether?

_____

Multiplying by 3	Multiplying by 4
When multiplying by 3, the answer is **three times** the number.	When multiplying by 4, the answer is **4 times the number.**

Multiplying by 3		Multiplying by 4	
3 x 0 = 0		4 x 0 = 0	
3 x 1 = 3	To work out 3 x 12, just do 12 + 12 + 12 so 3 lots of 12.	4 x 1 = 4	To work out 4 x 12, you can do: 12 + 12 + 12 + 12 or 2 x 12 = 24 and then 24 + 24 = 48
3 x 2 = 6		4 x 2 = 8	
3 x 3 = 9		4 x 3 = 12	
3 x 4 = 12		4 x 4 = 16	
3 x 5 = 15		4 x 5 = 20	
3 x 6 = 18		4 x 6 = 24	
3 x 7 = 21		4 x 7 = 28	
3 x 8 = 24		4 x 8 = 32	
3 x 9 = 27		4 x 9 = 36	
3 x 10 = 30		4 x 10 = 40	
3 x 11 = 33		4 x 11 = 44	
3 x 12 = 36		4 x 12 = 48	

7. Isla and her five friends go out for a drink. They buy a cup of coffee each. A cup of coffee costs £3. How much will they pay altogether?

_____

8. Noor is building a bench. She has three pieces of wood. Each piece is 9m long. How long are the three pieces altogether?

_____

9. Amar has bought three new sofas. Each sofa needs four non-slip stickers. How many non-slip stickers are needed for the three sofas?

_____

10. Rona has moved into a new home. She wants to buy four lamp shades. How much do four frames at £6 each cost?

_____

Multiplying by 5

When multiplying by 5, the answer is **5 times the number.**

$5 \times 0 = 0$
$5 \times 1 = 5$
$5 \times 2 = 10$
$5 \times 3 = 15$
$5 \times 4 = 20$
$5 \times 5 = 25$
$5 \times 6 = 30$
$5 \times 7 = 35$
$5 \times 8 = 40$
$5 \times 9 = 45$
$5 \times 10 = 50$
$5 \times 11 = 55$
$5 \times 12 = 60$

> To work out 5 x 12, you can do:
> 12 + 12 + 12 + 12 + 12
> or
> 2 x 12 = 24 and 24 + 24 = 48
> and 48 + 12 = 60
> or
> 12 x 10 = 120 and 120 ÷ 2 = 60

Multiplying by 6

When multiplying by 6, the answer is **6 times the number.**

$6 \times 0 = 0$
$6 \times 1 = 6$
$6 \times 2 = 12$
$6 \times 3 = 18$
$6 \times 4 = 24$
$6 \times 5 = 30$
$6 \times 6 = 36$
$6 \times 7 = 42$
$6 \times 8 = 48$
$6 \times 9 = 54$
$6 \times 10 = 60$
$6 \times 11 = 66$
$6 \times 12 = 72$

> To work out 6 x 12, you can do:
> 12 + 12 + 12 + 12 + 12 + 12
> or
> 2 x 12 = 24
> and 24 + 24 + 24 = 72
> or
> 3 x 12 = 36 and 36 + 36 = 72

11. Giovanni is counting how much money he has in his wallet. There are 12 five-euro notes in his wallet. How much money is in Giovanni's wallet?

_____

12. Helen can plant three plants in one hour. How many plants will she plant in five hours?

_____

13. A doctor can see six patients in one hour. How many patients can they see in four hours?

_____

Multiplying by 7

When multiplying by 7, the answer is **7 times the number.**

$7 \times 0 = 0$
$7 \times 1 = 7$
$7 \times 2 = 14$
$7 \times 3 = 21$
$7 \times 4 = 28$
$7 \times 5 = 35$
$7 \times 6 = 42$
$7 \times 7 = 49$
$7 \times 8 = 56$
$7 \times 9 = 63$
$7 \times 10 = 70$
$7 \times 11 = 77$
$7 \times 12 = 84$

> To work out 7 x 12, you can do:
> 12 + 12 + 12 + 12 + 12 + 12 + 12
> or
> 2 x 12 = 24 and 24 + 24 + 24 + 12 = 84
> or
> 3 x 12 = 36 and 36 + 36 + 12 = 84

Multiplying by 8

When multiplying by 8, the answer is **8 times the number.**

$8 \times 0 = 0$
$8 \times 1 = 8$
$8 \times 2 = 16$
$8 \times 3 = 24$
$8 \times 4 = 32$
$8 \times 5 = 40$
$8 \times 6 = 48$
$8 \times 7 = 56$
$8 \times 8 = 64$
$8 \times 9 = 72$
$8 \times 10 = 80$
$8 \times 11 = 88$
$8 \times 12 = 96$

> To work out 8 x 12, you can do:
> 12 + 12 + 12 + 12 + 12 + 12 + 12 + 12
> or
> 2 x 12 = 24 and 24 + 24 + 24 + 24 = 96
> or
> 4 x 12 = 48 and 48 + 48 = 96

14. Nafisha will save £10 each week for the next six weeks. How much will she save in total?

_____

15. There are seven cookies in one pack. How many cookies are there in six packs?

_____

16. Each day, Nev works 6 hours, from Monday to Sunday. How many hours does he work in a week?

_____

17. A family has eight members. Each family member is donating £5 to a charity. How much is the family donating altogether?

_____

18. Kay bought three notebooks at £8 each. How much did the notebooks cost altogether?

_____

Multiplying by 9

When multiplying by 9, the answer is **9 times the number.**

9 x 0 = 0
9 x 1 = 9
9 x 2 = 18
9 x 3 = 27
9 x 4 = 36
9 x 5 = 45
9 x 6 = 54
9 x 7 = 63
9 x 8 = 72
9 x 9 = 81
9 x 10 = 90
9 x 11 = 99
9 x 12 = 108

To work out 9 x 12, you can do:
12 + 12 + 12 + 12 + 12 + 12 + 12 +12 + 12
or
2 x 12 = 24 and 24 + 24 + 24 + 24 + 12 = 108
or
4 x 12 = 48 and 48 + 48 +12 = 108
or
3 x 12 = 36 and 36 + 36 + 36 = 108

---

19. In a school, there are 9 classes with 12 students in each class. How many students are there in total?

_____

20. One t-shirt costs £9. How much will five t-shirts cost?

_____

Multiplying by 10	Multiplying by 11
When multiplying by 10, the answer is **10 times the number.**	When multiplying by 11, the answer is **11 times the number.**

10 x 0 = 0	To work out 10 x 12, you can do:
10 x 1 = 10	12 x 10 = 120 (adding a 0 at the end)
10 x 2 = 20	or
10 x 3 = 30	2 x 12 = 24 and 24 + 24 + 24 + 24 + 24 = 120
10 x 4 = 40	or
10 x 5 = 50	5 x 12 = 60 and 60 + 60 = 120
10 x 6 = 60	
10 x 7 = 70	
10 x 8 = 80	
10 x 9 = 90	
10 x 10 = 100	
10 x 11 = 110	
10 x 12 = 120	

11 x 0 = 0	To work out 11 x 12, you can do:
11 x 1 = 11	12 x 10 = 120 and 120 + 12 = 132
11 x 2 = 22	or
11 x 3 = 33	5 x 12 = 60 and 60 + 60 + 12 = 132
11 x 4 = 44	
11 x 5 = 55	
11 x 6 = 66	
11 x 7 = 77	
11 x 8 = 88	
11 x 9 = 99	
11 x 10 = 110	
11 x 11 = 121	
11 x 12 = 132	

21 Li exercises for 10 minutes every day. How many minutes of exercise will he do in total, in ten days?

_____

22 Jim's phone bill is £10 a month. How much will pay in a year?

_____

23 The entry fee to a museum is £11. How much will it cost for six friends to visit the museum?

_____

Multiplying by 12

When multiplying by 12, the answer is 12 times the number.

12 x 0 = 0	To work out 12 x 12, you can do:
12 x 1 = 12	12 x 10 = 120 and 120 + 24 = 144
12 x 2 = 24	or
12 x 3 = 36	2 x 12 = 24 and 24 + 24 + 24 + 24 + 24 +24 = 144
12 x 4 = 48	or
12 x 5 = 60	3 x 12 = 36 and 36 + 36 + 36 + 36 = 144
12 x 6 = 72	or
12 x 7 = 84	4 x 12 = 48 and 48 + 48 + 48 = 144
12 x 8 = 96	or
12 x 9 = 108	6 x 12 = 72 and 72 + 72 = 144
12 x 10 = 120	
12 x 11 = 132	
12 x 12 = 144	

24. Zak has been given a mobile phone offer: 1 year contract. Pay £12 a month, get 1 month free. How much will the phone contract cost for one year?

_____

25. A cinema has 12 rows with 12 seats in each row. How many seats are there in total?

_____

26. A student pays £5 a month for a subscription. How much will the student pay for one year?

_____

> **Top Tips** Write the times tables facts on a grid and look at them again and again until you have learnt them by heart. Knowing the times tables is essential.

27. Fill the gaps.

1 x 0 =	2 x 0 =	3 x 0 =	4 x 0 =	5 x 0 =	6 x 0 =
1 x 1 =	2 x 1 =	3 x 1 =	4 x 1 =	5 x 1 =	6 x 1 =
1 x 2 =	2 x 2 =	3 x 2 =	4 x 2 =	5 x 2 =	6 x 2 =
1 x 3 =	2 x 3 =	3 x 3 =	4 x 3 =	5 x 3 =	6 x 3 =
1 x 4 =	2 x 4 =	3 x 4 =	4 x 4 =	5 x 4 =	6 x 4 =
1 x 5 =	2 x 5 =	3 x 5 =	4 x 5 =	5 x 5 =	6 x 5 =
1 x 6 =	2 x 6 =	3 x 6 =	4 x 6 =	5 x 6 =	6 x 6 =
1 x 7 =	2 x 7 =	3 x 7 =	4 x 7 =	5 x 7 =	6 x 7 =
1 x 8 =	2 x 8 =	3 x 8 =	4 x 8 =	5 x 8 =	6 x 8 =
1 x 9 =	2 x 9 =	3 x 9 =	4 x 9 =	5 x 9 =	6 x 9 =
1 x 10 =	2 x 10 =	3 x 10 =	4 x 10 =	5 x 10 =	6 x 10 =
1 x 11 =	2 x 11 =	3 x 11 =	4 x 11 =	5 x 11 =	6 x 11 =
1 x 12 =	2 x 12 =	3 x 12 =	4 x 12 =	5 x 12 =	6 x 12 =

7 x 0 =	8 x 0 =	9 x 0 =	10 x 0 =	11 x 0 =	12 x 0 =
7 x 1 =	8 x 1 =	9 x 1 =	10 x 1 =	11 x 1 =	12 x 1 =
7 x 2 =	8 x 2 =	9 x 2 =	10 x 2 =	11 x 2 =	12 x 2 =
7 x 3 =	8 x 3 =	9 x 3 =	10 x 3 =	11 x 3 =	12 x 3 =
7 x 4 =	8 x 4 =	9 x 4 =	10 x 4 =	11 x 4 =	12 x 4 =
7 x 5 =	8 x 5 =	9 x 5 =	10 x 5 =	11 x 5 =	12 x 5 =
7 x 6 =	8 x 6 =	9 x 6 =	10 x 6 =	11 x 6 =	12 x 6 =
7 x 7 =	8 x 7 =	9 x 7 =	10 x 7 =	11 x 7 =	12 x 7 =
7 x 8 =	8 x 8 =	9 x 8 =	10 x 8 =	11 x 8 =	12 x 8 =
7 x 9 =	8 x 9 =	9 x 9 =	10 x 9 =	11 x 9 =	12 x 9 =
7 x 10 =	8 x 10 =	9 x 10 =	10 x 10 =	11 x 10 =	12 x 10 =
7 x 11 =	8 x 11 =	9 x 11 =	10 x 11 =	11 x 11 =	12 x 11 =
7 x 12 =	8 x 12 =	9 x 12 =	10 x 12 =	11 x 12 =	12 x 12 =

28. Nara works 7 hours a day. She works from Monday to Friday. She thinks she works 40 hours a week. Is this correct? Why?

_____

29 Fill the gaps.

1 x 10 =	2 x 0 =	3 x 7 =	5 x 0 =	5 x 11 =	6 x 3 =
4 x 1 =	8 x 1 =	3 x 8 =	4 x 6 =	5 x 12 =	6 x 2 =
6 x 2 =	7 x 2 =	3 x 4 =	4 x 8 =	5 x 7 =	6 x 6 =
9 x 3 =	4 x 3 =	9 x 3 =	4 x 3 =	5 x 5 =	6 x 4 =
8 x 4 =	9 x 4 =	4 x 4 =	4 x 9 =	6 x 4 =	6 x 8 =
3 x 5 =	6 x 5 =	8 x 5 =	4 x 6 =	5 x 5 =	6 x 9 =
6 x 6 =	2 x 6 =	5 x 6 =	7 x 6 =	3 x 6 =	6 x 10 =
9 x 7 =	3 x 7 =	3 x 7 =	9 x 7 =	8 x 7 =	8 x 7 =
4 x 8 =	6 x 8 =	9 x 8 =	11 x 8 =	4 x 8 =	9 x 8 =
6 x 9 =	4 x 9 =	2 x 9 =	1 x 9 =	9 x 9 =	4 x 9 =
5 x 10 =	6 x 10 =	10 x 10 =	12 x 10 =	4 x 10 =	9 x 10 =
9 x 11 =	7 x 11 =	6 x 11 =	4 x 11 =	6 x 11 =	7 x 11 =
10 x 12 =	2 x 12 =	12 x 12 =	4 x 12 =	8 x 12 =	5 x 12 =

30 Fill the gaps.

x	0	1	2	3	4	5	6	7	8	9	10	11	12
0													
1													
2													
3													
4													
5													
6													
7													
8													
9													
10													
11													
12													

31 Van is buying 3 boxes with cupcakes. In each box there are 12 cupcakes. Does she have enough for 35 people? Why?

_____

32 Heather says 'any number multiplied by 0, equals 0'. Is she correct?

_____

33 Fill the gaps.

3 x ___ = 15	3 x ___ = 15	3 x ___ = 15	3 x ___ = 15	3 x ___ = 15	3 x ___ = 15
6 x ___ = 24	6 x ___ = 24	6 x ___ = 24	6 x ___ = 24	6 x ___ = 24	6 x ___ = 24

34

a) A jar of honey costs £6.
How much do three jars cost?

_____

b) There are five cookies in a bag.
How many cookies are there in five bags?

_____

c) A bag of pasta weighs 1 kg.
How much will ten bags weigh?

_____

d) A bag of flour weighs 2 kg.
How much will four bags weigh?

_____

e) There are two fish in a pack.
Gela needs 7 fish.
Will three packs be enough?

_____

f) A milk bottle fills four glasses.
Tracey drinks one glass of milk each day.
Will three bottles be enough for two weeks?

_____

g) A box of cereal costs £2.
Are £10 enough for five boxes?

_____

h) A bottle of catch up lasts a family six week:
How many weeks will six bottles last for?

_____

i) Drew has a cartoon with ten eggs in the fridge. She is making three cakes, using four eggs in each cake. How many more eggs are needed?

_____

35 Fill the gaps.

2	4	6									
5	10	15									
			35	42	49						
							32	36	40		
			27	36	45						
									60	66	72
8	16	24									
			12	15	18						
						77	88	98	110	121	132

36 Dea says '4 x 8 is the same as 2 x 8 and 2 x 8. Is this correct?

_____

There are two ways to work out the total number of chocolate squares.

Order doesn't matter when multiplying.
Example: 4 x 3 = 1 2   3 x 4 = 12

3 rows with 6 squares each: 6 columns with 3 squares each:
3 x 6 = 18   6 x 3 = 18   76

Here are some more examples.

  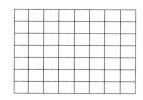

4 x 6 represents the same amount as 6 x 4   8 x 7 represents the same amount as 7 x 8

Fill the gaps.

37

| 7 x 5 is the same as 5 x 7 | 2 x 10 is the same as 10 x ___ | 12 x 4 is the same as 4 x ___ |
| 5 x 6 is the same as 6 x ___ | 11 x 3 is the same as ___ x 11 | 7 x 8 is the same as 8 x ___ |

Progress check

1 You go shopping and buy 3 packs of baked beans cans. There are 6 cans in each pack. How many cans did you buy altogether?

_____

2 Write a multiplication sentence to represent the number of squares shown below.

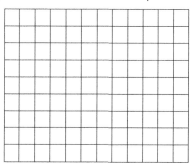

___ x ___ = ___

Fill in the gaps.

3

| 5 x 10 = ___ | 4 x ___ = 32 | ___ x 6 = 36 |

4 Naila writes these maths sentences:

| 6 x 4 = 4 x 6 | 1 x 5 = 1 | 5 x 0 = 5 |

Do you agree with Naila? Explain your answer.

_____

5 Find another two numbers you can multiply which give the same total as 8 x 3:

___ x ___

Divide two-digit whole numbers by single-digit whole numbers

1nd express remainders

We use division when:
➢ sharing items equally with others
➢ working out pay per hour, knowing pay per day
➢ calculating price per item when buying a pack
➢ sharing food in portions
➢ planning exercise routines

Example: Sonia has 14 apples. She is sharing them equally with her friend, Dan.

14 ÷ 2 = 7   They get 7 apples each.

Example: Ben has £15. He will share it equally with his two friends, Desi and Norma. How much will each of them get?

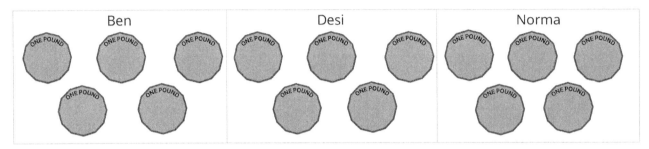

15 ÷ 3 = 5   They get £5 each.

Here is the times tables grid. How can the grid help? What is the link with times tables?

x	0	1	2	3	4	5	6	7	8	9	10	11	12
0	0	0	0	0	0	0	0	0	0	0	0	0	0
1	0	1	2	3	4	5	6	7	8	9	10	11	12
2	0	2	4	6	8	10	12	14	16	18	20	22	24
3	0	3	6	9	12	15	18	21	24	27	30	33	36
4	0	4	8	12	16	20	24	28	32	36	40	44	48
5	0	5	10	15	20	25	30	35	40	45	50	55	60
6	0	6	12	18	24	30	36	42	48	54	60	66	72
7	0	7	14	21	28	35	42	49	56	63	70	77	84
8	0	8	16	24	32	40	48	56	64	72	80	88	96
9	0	9	18	27	36	45	54	63	72	81	90	99	108
10	0	10	20	30	40	50	60	70	80	90	100	110	120
11	0	11	22	33	44	55	66	77	88	99	110	121	132
12	0	12	24	36	48	60	72	84	96	108	120	131	144

48 ÷ 4 = 12

48 ÷ 12 = 4

What do you notice?

Division is the opposite of multiplication.

Work out.

| 10 ÷ 2 = ___ | 40 ÷ 4 = ___ | 24 ÷ 6 = ___ | 42 ÷ 6 = ___ | 63 ÷ 7 = ___ |

| 15 ÷ 5 = ___ | 32 ÷ 8 = ___ | 16 ÷ 4 = ___ | 64 ÷ 8 = ___ | 100 ÷ 10 = ___ |
| 21 ÷ 3 = ___ | 16 ÷ 2 = ___ | 18 ÷ 3 = ___ | 81 ÷ 9 = ___ | 40 ÷ 5 = ___ |

A chocolate bar has 18 squares. The chocolate bar has 6 columns. How many squares are there in each column? There are different ways to divide the total number of chocolate squares.

18 ÷ 3 = 6 There are 6 squares in each row.   18 ÷ 6 = 3 There are 3 squares in each column.

When dividing large numbers, we start with the tens.
Example: 42p ÷ 2

We start by sharing the 10p coins first:

Then sharing the 1p coins too:

Each person gets 21p.

Example: 69 ÷ 3

We start by sharing the blocks of 10 first:

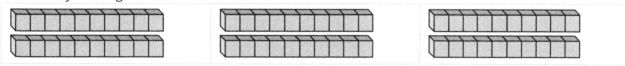

Then sharing the ones too:

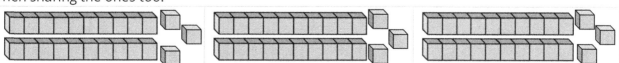

Each person gets 23.

Division without regrouping

79

 Example 1

$48 \div 4$

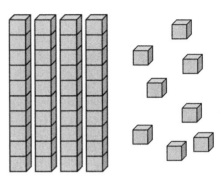

Visual representation:

Step 1

Write the calculation correctly.

Step 2

How many groups of 4 can we make with the tens?

Only 1, as $4 \div 4 = 1$

We write the answer at the top.

$$\begin{array}{c} 1 \\ 4\,\overline{|\ \ 4\quad 8} \end{array}$$

Visual representation:

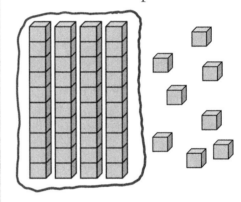

Step 3

How many groups of 4 can we make with the ones?

Only 2, as $8 \div 4 = 2$

We write the answer at the top.

$$\begin{array}{c} 1\quad 2 \\ 4\,\overline{|\ \ 4\quad 8} \end{array}$$

There are no more digits left, so $48 \div 4 = 12$ or $4 \times 12 = 48$

Visual representation:

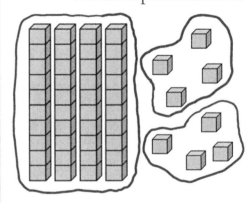

There are no more cubes left, so we've finished dividing.

 **Example 2**

$$60 \div 3$$

Visual representation:

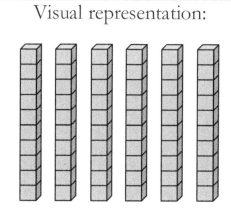

Step 1

Write the calculation correctly.

$$3 \overline{) \quad 6 \quad 0 }$$

Step 2

How many groups of 3 can we make with the tens?

Only 2, as 6 ÷ 3 = 2

We write the answer at the top.

$$3 \overline{) \quad 6 \quad 0 }^{\,2}$$

Visual representation:

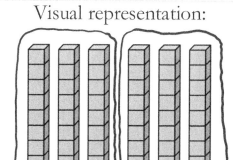

Step 3

How many groups of 3 can we make with the ones?

0 as 0 ÷ 3 = 0

We write the answer at the top.

$$3 \overline{) \quad 6 \quad 0 }^{\,2 \quad 0}$$

There are no more digits left, so 60 ÷ 3 = 20 or 3 x 20 = 60

Visual representation:

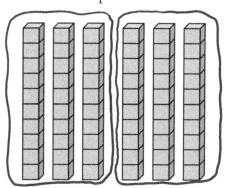

There are no more cubes left, so we've finished dividing.

Here are some more examples.

	2 1		2 3		3 0
4	8 4	3	6 9	2	6 0

Work out. Use a calculator to check your answers.

2

46 ÷ 2 =	93 ÷ 3 =	84 ÷ 4 =	84 ÷ 2 =	55 ÷ 5 =	60 ÷ 6 =
66 ÷ 2 =	63 ÷ 3 =	48 ÷ 4 =	90 ÷ 3 =	77 ÷ 7 =	88 ÷ 2 =
39 ÷ 3 =	50 ÷ 5 =	82 ÷ 2 =	96 ÷ 3 =	88 ÷ 4 =	66 ÷ 3 =

Answer these division questions.

3

a) Dan spent £36 on buying 3 identical vases. How much did one vase cost?	b) Lola has three children and 30 sweets. She will share them equally between her children. How many sweets will each child get?	c) Buses come to a bus stop every 5 minutes. How many buses will come in 55 minutes?
d) There are 4 cookies in a pack. Nala needs 84 cookies for a party. How many packs should she buy?	e) Ben wants to walk for 69 minutes over 3 days. How many minutes will Ben walk each day, if he does the same number of minutes?	f)Mini is building a bench. She needs pieces of wood that are 2m long. How many 2m pieces can she make with 26m?

4 Asma is dividing 60 by 3 and thinks the answer is 2. What did she do wrong?

_____

Example 1

$$42 \div 3$$

Visual representation:

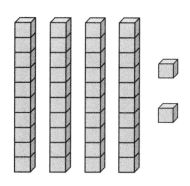

Step 1

Write the calculation correctly.

$$3 \overline{\smash{\big)}\ 4 \quad 2}$$

Step 2

Visual representation:

How many groups of 3 can we make with the tens?

Only 1 as $4 \div 3 = 1$ with 1 remaining. The remaining 1 is a group of 10.

We write the answer at the top.

$$3 \overline{\smash{\big)}\ \overset{1}{4} \quad 2}$$

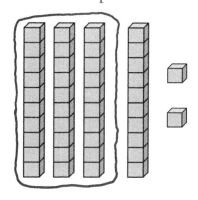

Step 3

Visual representation:

How many groups of 3 can we make with the ones?

Only 4, as $12 \div 3 = 4$

We write the answer at the top.

$$3 \overline{\smash{\big)}\ \overset{1\quad 4}{4 \quad 2}}$$

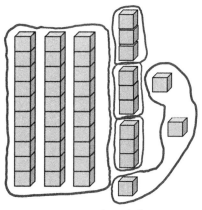

There are no more cubes left, so we've finished dividing.

There are no more digits left, so $42 \div 3 = 14$ or $3 \times 14 = 42$

 Example 2

75 ÷ 5

Visual representation:

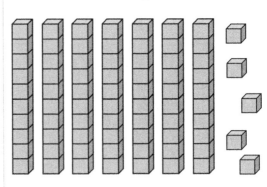

Step 1

Write the calculation correctly.

$$5 \overline{\smash{)}75}$$

Step 2

How many groups of 5 can we make with the tens?

Only 1, as 7 ÷ 5 = 1 with 2 remaining. The remaining 2 are groups of 10, so have a value of 20.

We write the answer at the top.

$$5 \overline{\smash{)}\,7^{\,2}\,5}^{\,1}$$

Visual representation:

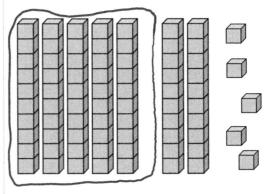

Step 3

How many groups of 5 can we make with the ones?

5 as 25 ÷ 5 = 5

We write the answer at the top.

$$5 \overline{\smash{)}\,7^{\,2}\,5}^{\,15}$$

There are no more digits left, so 75 ÷ 5 = 15 or 5 x 15 = 75

Visual representation:

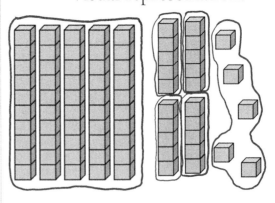

There are no more cubes left, so we've finished dividing.

Here are some more examples.

2 4	2 6	3 6
4) 9 6	3) 8 4	2) 7 2

5 Work out. Use a calculator to check your answers.

56 ÷ 2 =	72 ÷ 3 =	96 ÷ 4 =	94 ÷ 2 =	75 ÷ 5 =	84 ÷ 6 =
96 ÷ 2 =	84 ÷ 3 =	60 ÷ 4 =	87 ÷ 3 =	91 ÷ 7 =	54 ÷ 2 =
48 ÷ 3 =	90 ÷ 5 =	96 ÷ 2 =	57 ÷ 3 =	56 ÷ 4 =	72 ÷ 2 =

6 Answer these division questions.

a) Dan spent £42 on buying 3 identical plant pots. How much did one plant pot cost? _____	b) Lola has three children and 48 cherries. She will share them equally between her children. How many cherries will each child get? _____	c) Buses come to a bus stop every 5 minutes. How many buses will come in 65 minutes? _____
d) There are 4 drinks in a pack. Nala needs 72 drinks for a party. How many packs should she buy? _____	e) Ben wants to walk for 78 minutes over 3 days. How many minutes will Ben walk each day, if he does the same number of minutes? _____	f)Mini is building a dog house. She needs pieces of wood that are 2m long. How many 2m pieces can she make with 36m? _____

7 Asma is dividing 72 by 3 and thinks the answer is 20. What did she do wrong?

_____

Example 1

$$77 \div 3$$

Step 1

Write the calculation correctly.

$$3 \overline{)\ 7 \quad 7}$$

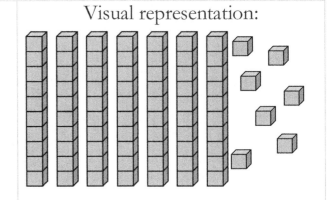

Visual representation:

Step 2

How many groups of 3 can we make with the tens?

Only 2, as 7 ÷ 3 = 2 rem 1

We write the answer at the top.

$$3 \overline{)\ 7^2 \quad 7} \quad {}^{2}$$

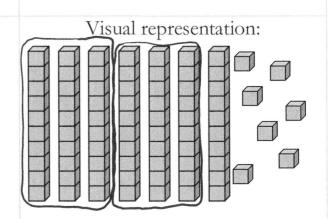

Visual representation:

Step 3

How many groups of 3 can we make with the ones?

5 as 17 ÷ 3 = 5 with 2 remaining.

We write the answer at the top.

$$3 \overline{)\ 7^2 \quad 7} \quad {}^{2} \quad 5 \text{ remaining } 2$$

There are no more digits left, so 77 ÷ 3 = 25 rem 2

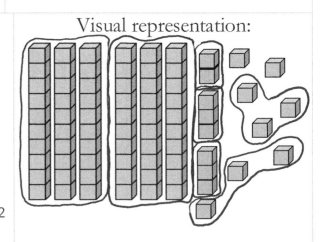

Visual representation:

Example 2

$$69 \div 5$$

Visual representation:

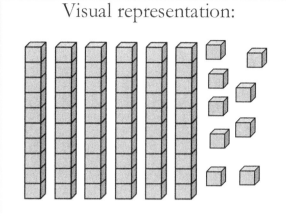

Step 1

Write the calculation correctly.

$$5 \overline{)69}$$

Visual representation:

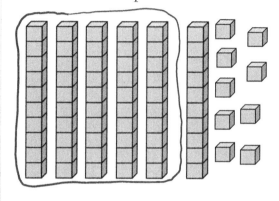

Step 2

How many groups of 5 can we make with the tens?

Only 1, as 6 ÷ 5 = 1 with 1 remaining. The remaining 1 is a group of 10.

We write the answer at the top.

$$5 \overline{)6^{1}9}^{\displaystyle 1}$$

Visual representation:

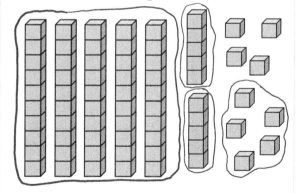

Step 3

How many groups of 5 can we make with the ones?

3 as 19 ÷ 5 = 3 with 4 remaining

We write the answer at the top.

$$\overset{\displaystyle 1 \qquad 3 \text{ remaining } 4}{5 \overline{)6^{1}9}}$$

There are no more digits left, so 69 ÷ 5 = 13 rem 4

Here are some more examples.

	1	4 rem 4			1	1 rem 3			2	4 rem 3
5	7	4		4	6	7		4	9	9

8 Work out. Use a calculator to check your answer.

57 ÷ 2 =	74 ÷ 3 =	98 ÷ 4 =	95 ÷ 2 =	77 ÷ 5 =	87 ÷ 6 =
97 ÷ 2 =	85 ÷ 3 =	61 ÷ 4 =	88 ÷ 3 =	97 ÷ 7 =	55 ÷ 2 =
50 ÷ 3 =	93 ÷ 5 =	97 ÷ 2 =	59 ÷ 3 =	59 ÷ 4 =	49 ÷ 3 =

9 Answer these division questions.

a) Dan has £86. He wants to buy as many socks as possible. Each pair cost £7.

How many pairs can he buy?

_____

How much money will have left?

_____

b) Lola has three children and 50 pens. She will share them equally between her children.

How many pens will each child get?

_____

How many pens are left over?

_____

c) Ben has 35 apples. He will make as many pies as possible. Each pie requires four apples.

How many pies will he make?

_____

How many apples are left over?

_____

d) There are 4 cupcakes in a pack. Nala needs 75 cupcakes for a party.

How many packs should she buy?

_____

e) Buses come to a bus stop every 5 minutes.

How many buses will come in 67 minutes?

_____

f) Mini is building a fence. She needs pieces of wood that are 2m long.

How many 2m pieces can she make with 37m?

_____

10 Asma is dividing 74 by 3 and thinks the answer is 24.2. What did she do wrong?

_____

The long division method

The long division method is like the other method; you just show the working out rather than doing it in your head.

2 8	1 4	1 3
3) 8 4	4) 5 6	6) 7 8
- 6	- 4	- 6
2 4	1 6	1 8
- 2 4	- 1 6	- 1 8
0	0	0

2 8 rem 2	1 4 rem 3	1 3 rem 2
3) 8 6	4) 5 9	6) 8 0
- 6	- 4	- 6
2 6	1 9	2 0
- 2 4	- 1 6	- 1 8
2	3	2

2 4 rem 2	1 3 rem 4	1 1 rem 6
3) 7 4	5) 6 9	7) 8 3
- 6	- 5	- 7
1 4	1 9	1 3
- 1 2	- 1 5	- 0 7
2	4	6

You can use any division method you like. You don't need to use a specific method.

11) a) There are 12 yogurt pots in 3 packs. How many are there in each pack?

_____

b) Two cans of soup costs 80p. How much does one can cost?

_____

c) A packet of crisps has 6 small packets inside. How many big packets do you need to get 18 small packets.

_____

d) There are 20 cookies and 5 people. How many will each of them get, if they share them equally?

_____

e) A cake is divided into nine slices. Three people share them equally. How many slices will each person get?

_____

f) A group of students raised £50 for charity. They will split the amount equally between 5 charities. How much will each charity get?

_____

g) A can of tuna costs £1. How many can you buy with £10?

_____

h) There are 60 chocolates in a box. Five friends share them equally. How many will each get?

_____

Use a calculator to divide these numbers.

$16 ÷ 4 =$ _____ and $4 ÷ 16 =$ _____

$20 ÷ 5 =$ _____ and $5 ÷ 20 =$ _____

$10 ÷ 2 =$ _____ and $2 ÷ 10 =$ _____

$25 ÷ 5 =$ _____ and $5 ÷ 25 =$ _____

What do you notice?

Order matters when dividing. Example: $4 ÷ 2 = 2$ and $2 ÷ 4 = 0.5$

12) A class of 52 students needs to be divided into groups of 4 for a project. The teacher works out how many groups can be formed: $52 ÷ 4 = 13$ Is the teacher correct?

_____

13) Hana has 54 pieces of wood and needs to put them into 3 equal stacks. She works out how many pieces of wood will be in each stack? $3 ÷ 54 = 18$ Is Hana correct?

_____

Language is important!
4 **divided by** 2:
Example: $4 ÷ 2$

14) Jenny plants 88 flowers in 8 equal rows. She works out how many flowers are planted in each row: $88 ÷ 8 = 11$ Is Jenny correct?

_____

15) Anna shares twelve tasks equally between her three children. She thinks each of them will get four. Is Anna correct?

_____

> Dividing a number by 0, gives you no answer.
> Example: 8 ÷ 0 is undefined. (Imagine having 8 apples and putting them in no groups)

16. Heather says 'any number divided by 0, equals 0'. Is she correct?

_____

The link between multiplication and division

3 x ___ = 15 is the same as 15 ÷ 3 = ___
___ x 7 = 14 is the same as 14 ÷ 7 = ___

> Multiplication ⬌ Division
> Multiplication is the opposite of division.
> Division is the opposite of multiplication.

17. Fill the gaps.

6 x ___ = 12 is the same as <u>12 ÷ 6</u>	___ x 7 = 21 is the same as <u>21 ÷ 7</u>
9 x ___ = 27 is the same as _____	___ x 5 = 35 is the same as _____
5 x ___ = 20 is the same as _____	___ x 7 = 42 is the same as _____
8 x ___ = 32 is the same as _____	___ x 11 = 66 is the same as _____

18. Fill the gaps.

3 x 4 = 12 so 12 ÷ 3 = ____ and 12 ÷ 4 = ____	9 x 3 = 27 so 27 ÷ 3 = ____ and 27 ÷ 9 = ____
7 x 5 = 35 so 35 ÷ 5 = ____ and 35 ÷ 7 = ____	10 x 6 = 60 so 60 ÷ 10 = ____ and 60 ÷ 6 = ____
6 x 8 = 48 so 48 ÷ 6 = ____ and 48 ÷ 8 = ____	8 x 11 = 88 so 88 ÷ 8 = ____ and 88 ÷ 11 = ____
4 x 7 = 28 so 28 ÷ 4 = ____ and 28 ÷ 7 = ____	4 x 12 = 48 so 48 ÷ 4 = ____ and 48 ÷ 12 = ____

The link between addition, subtraction, multiplication and division

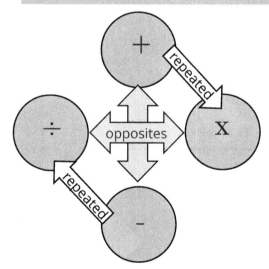

> **Subtraction** is the opposite of **addition**.
> Example: 4 + 3 = 7   7 – 3 = 4
>
> **Division** is the opposite of **multiplication**.
> Example: 4 x 3 = 12   12 ÷ 4 = 3
>
> **Multiplication** is repeated **addition**.
> Example: 3 x 4 is the same as 4 + 4 + 4
>
> **Division** is repeated **subtraction**.
> Example: 12 ÷ 3 is the same as 12 - 3 - 3 - 3 - 3

We use the opposite calculation to check an answer.
To check addition, we use subtraction. To check subtraction, we use addition. To check multiplication, we use division or repeated addition. To check division, we use multiplication or repeated subtraction.

Checking answers

Example: Danny is buying a pair of shoes for £36 and a shirt for £23. How much do these cost in total? 36 + 23 = 59   To check the answer: 59 – 23 = 36 or 59 – 36 = 23

Example: Oliver has £100 in his bank account. He spends £74 on groceries. What is the new bank balance after buying groceries? 100 – 74 = 26   To check: 26 + 74 = 100 or 74 + 26 = 100

Example: There are 8 cookies in a pack. How many cookies are there in 3 packs? 3 x 8 = 24
To check: 24 ÷ 3 =8 or 24 ÷ 8 = 3 or 8 + 8 + 8 = 24

Example: Zara works 35 hours a week. She works from Monday to Friday. How many hours a day does Zara work for? 35 ÷ 5 = 7   To check: 7 x 5 = 35 or 5 x 7 = 35 or 35 – 7 – 7 – 7 – 7 – 7

19 There are two maths classes in a college. One class has 27 students and the other has 25 students. How many maths students are there altogether?

_____

Check your answer:

_____

20 84 people have booked a table in a restaurant. 38 people have already arrived. How many more are expected to arrive?

_____

Check your answer:

_____

21 Ben spends 90 minutes a week exercising. He exercises from Monday to Saturday. How many minutes does Ben spend exercising each day?

_____

Check your answer:

_____

22 Sukhdev pays a monthly subscription of £8 for an app. How much will he pay for the whole year?

_____

Check your answer:

_____

23 Dea works 7 hours a day. She earns £12 per hour. How much does she earn per day?

_____

Check your answer:

_____

24. Nikki is planting so flowers in the garden. It took her 30 minutes to plant the flowers. Planting one flower took her three minutes. How many flowers did she plant in total?

_____

Check your answer:

_____

You only need to use one method to check your answer.

25. Check these calculations.

18 + 18 = 36   Check: _____   28 - 16 = 14   Check: _____

5 x 4 = 20   Check: _____   29 + 36 = 65   Check: _____

10 + 68 = 78   Check: _____   42 ÷ 7 = 6   Check: _____

56 ÷ 8 = 7   Check: _____   37 - 6 = 31   Check: _____

26. Nisa says: 'For multiplication you have two ways of checking: division and addition'. Is she correct?

_____

27. Liam will run 84 miles in 12 weeks. He will run the same distance every week. He works out how many miles he will run per week: 12 ÷ 84 = 7   Is Liam correct?

_____

Progress check

1. Ann is organizing a party. She wants to buy 15 drinks. Drinks come in packs of six. How many packs does she need to buy?

_____

Check your answer.

_____

2. Maya spends the same amount of money on fruit every week. She spent £64 in February (4 weeks). How much does Maya spend on fruit every week?   ___ ÷ ___ = ___

Check your answer.

_____

3. Fill in the gaps below:

| 36 ÷ 9 = ___ | 50 ÷ 10 = ___ | 63 ÷ ___ = 7 | 64 ÷ 7 = _____ |

4. Naila writes these maths sentences: 16 ÷ 4 = 4 ÷ 16   5 ÷ 1 = 1
Do you agree with Naila? Explain your answer.

_____

5. Jo worked out that 42 ÷ 7 = 6 . How can she check that her answer by multiplying?   ___ x ___ = ___

93

Recognise and interpret symbols for + , - , x , ÷ and = appropriately

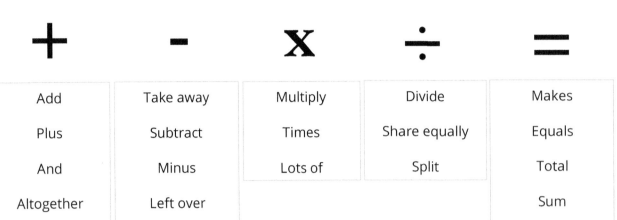

Add	Take away	Multiply	Divide	Makes
Plus	Subtract	Times	Share equally	Equals
And	Minus	Lots of	Split	Total
Altogether	Left over			Sum
More	Less			Same as
Total	Fewer			
	Difference			

1 ▷ Add the missing symbols (+ - x ÷ =)

6 + 4 ___ 10	8 ___ 3 = 11	6 ___ 2 = 3	4 x 3 ___ 12	8 ___ 4 = 4
10 ___ 4 = 6	17 – 2 ___ 15	16 ___ 2 = 8	3 x 3 ___ 9	20 ___ 20 = 40
12 ___ 3 = 15	10 ___ 0 = 10	4 ___ 4 = 16	20 ___ 20 = 0	24 ___ 4 = 6
15 ___ 3 = 12	15 + 5 ___ 20	15 ___ 5 = 20	72 ___ 8 = 9	8 ___ 4 = 12

2 ▷ Femi is adding 47 and 33. Show how Femi can add 47 and 33.

47 - 33		33 - 47		47 + 33		47 x 33

Tick the correct option.

3 ▷ Sona is working out 33 days take away 16. Show how Sona can work out 33 take away 16.

33 - 16		16 - 33		33 x 16		33 ÷ 16

Tick the correct option.

4 ▷ Jo is working out 71 minus 46. Show how Jo can work out 71 minus 46.

71 + 46		71 - 46		71 ÷ 46		71 x 46

Tick the correct option.

5 ▷ Maya works 35 hours a week. She works from Monday to Friday and does the same number of hours each day. Maya wants to work out how many hours of work she does each day.

6 ▷ Saj takes the train to college every week. He goes to college four days a week. The cost of one return ticket is £4. Saj wants to work out how much he spends on train tickets to travel to college every week.

7 ▷ Tom spends 35 hours a week studying. He studies from Sunday to Thursday and dedicates the same amount of time to it each day. Tom wants to figure out how many hours she studies each day.

8 ▷ Olivia runs six days a week. She runs 7 kilometers each day. How many kilometers does she run each week?

9 ▷ A bakery makes and distributes 50 loaves of bread every day. They distribute 32 loaves in the morning. How many do they distribute in the afternoon?

10 ▷ a) What is the symbol for division? _____ b) What is the symbol for multiplication? _____

11 ▷ Match the terms that mean the same.

Subtract	**+**	More
Makes		Equals
Total	**-**	Left over
Lots of		Plus
Add	**=**	And
Take away		Share equally
Divide	**X**	Subtract from
Minus		Altogether
Times	**÷**	Multiply

In the calculator, this is how the symbols look like:

To work out: 25 + 7 , you press:

| 2 | 5 | + | 7 | = |

To work out: 39 - 14 , you press:

| 3 | 9 | - | 1 | 4 | = |

To work out: 8 x 6 , you press:

| 8 | x | 6 | = |

To work out: 49 ÷ 7 , you press:

| 4 | 9 | ÷ | 7 | = |

add
subtract
multiply
divide

decimal point   equal

To clear calculations, you press the C button in the calculator.

12 Use a calculator to work out:

| 53 + 48 = | 93 - 54 = | 56 - 37 = | 0 x 12 = | 10 x 10 = | 12 ÷ 3 = |
| 63 + 67 = | 47 - 26 = | 70 + 10 = | 40 ÷ 5 = | 12 x 8 = | 42 ÷ 7 = |

13 Work out the answer to these calculations and then check using a calculator.

| 48 + 68 = | 63 - 44 = | 45 + 72 = | 4 x 9 = | 10 x 10 = | 18 ÷ 3 = |
| 50 + 30 = | 87 - 25 = | 76 - 39 = | 45 ÷ 5 = | 7 x 8 = | 42 ÷ 3 = |

14 There are 46 chairs in the waiting area. 11 patients are sitting in the waiting area. How many chairs are empty? Check your answer using a calculator.

_____

15 Oli has invited 35 friends to a party. 28 friends arrived at the party. How many more friends should come to the party? Check your answer using a calculator.

_____

16 Pat sells cinema tickets. She has sold 9 tickets at £7 each. How much money has Pat made from the tickets she has sold? Check your answer using a calculator.

_____

17 Sylvia spends £28 on bus tickets every week. She travels seven days a week. How much does Sylvia spend each day on bus tickets? Check your answer using a calculator.

_____

18 Dan walks for 10 minutes in the morning every day. How many minutes does Dan walk in total a week? Check your answer using a calculator.

_____

19 Sarah reads 98 Pages of her book over seven days. If she reads the same number of pages every day, how many pages does she read per day? Check your answer using a calculator.

_____

Mental Methods: Number bonds

When adding and subtracting, it is very useful to know the number bonds. Number bonds are pairs of numbers that total 5 or any other number.

These are the pairs of numbers that make 5. These are called **number bonds to 5**.

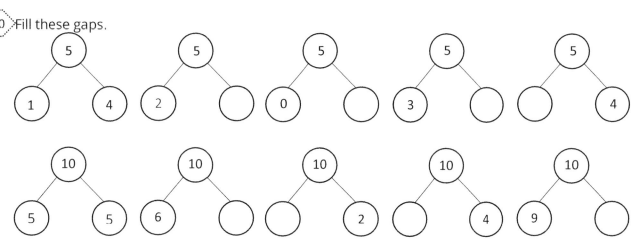

20 Fill these gaps.

21 Fill these gaps:

1 + ___ = 5	2 + ___ = 5	___ + 4 = 5	___ + 5 = 5	___ + 3 = 5
3 + ___ = 5	4 + ___ = 5	___ + 2 = 5	3 + 2 = ___	___ + 1 = 5
0 + ___ = 10	1 + ___ = 10	___ + 7 = 10	___ + 0 = 10	2 + ___ = 10
3 + ___ = 10	4 + ___ = 10	___ + 6 = 10	___ + 2 = 10	5 + ___ = 10
6 + ___ = 10	7 + ___ = 10	___ + 4 = 10	___ + 9 = 10	8 + ___ = 10

Mental methods: Compensation

When adding 53 and 9:
As 9 is close to 10, **add 10 and take away 1**.

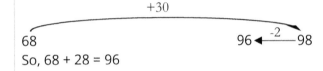

So, 53 + 9 = 62

When subtracting 19 from 72:
As 19 is close to 20, **take away 20 and add 1**.

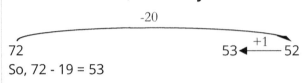

So, 72 - 19 = 53

When adding 68 and 28:
As 28 is close to 30, **add 30 and take away 2**.

68 +30 ... 96 ←-2— 98

So, 68 + 28 = 96

When subtracting 37 from 95:
As 37 is close to 40, **subtract 40 and add 3**.

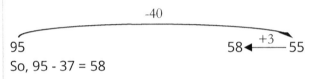

So, 95 - 37 = 58

22 Fill the gaps.

35 + 9 = ___

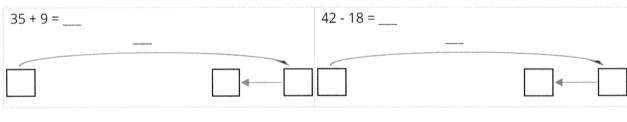

42 - 18 = ___

56 + 27 = ___

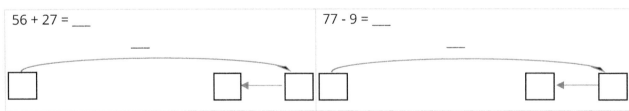

77 - 9 = ___

77 + 28 = ___

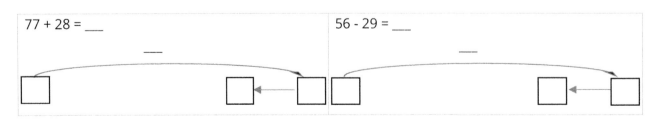

56 - 29 = ___

Mental methods: Reordering

When adding: 6 + 8 + 4	When taking away: 17 – 4 – 7
6 + 4 = 10 (number bonds)	17 - 7 = 10
10 + 8 = 18	10 - 4 = 6 (number bonds)

23 Fill the gaps.

5 + 9 + 5 =

☐ + ☐ = ☐

☐ + ☐ = ☐

25 – 6 - 5 =

☐ - ☐ = ☐

☐ - ☐ = ☐

11 + 7 + 9 =

☐ + ☐ = ☐

☐ + ☐ = ☐

38 – 3 - 8 =

☐ - ☐ = ☐

☐ - ☐ = ☐

Progress check

1 Match these symbols with their meaning.

x	divide
-	add
=	equals
÷	multiply
+	subtract

2 Fill in the boxes below with one of these symbols: +, - , x , ÷ or = , so that the sentence is true.

6 ☐ 5 = 11   12 ÷ 4 ☐ 3   20 ☐ 8 = 12

2 ☐ 7 = 14   12 ÷ 3 ☐ 4   5 ☐ 1 = 5

3 Write another two words that represent the meaning of the symbol.

x   times, _____ , _____   ÷   _____ , share equally, _____

4 Nev writes: 5 = 10 - 2   He's made a mistake. What mistake has he made? Correct his answer.

_____

5 Arfa had 80p in her pocket. She bought a pack of biscuits for 50p. How do you work out how much money she has left?

_____

Approximate by rounding to the nearest 10, and use this answer to check results

We round when:
> working out the total cost of items we have bought
> checking that we have done calculations correctly
> estimating the cost of bills over time
> estimating the time it takes to travel to a place

To round to the nearest 10, means to decide which of the tens the number is closest to.

Example: 39

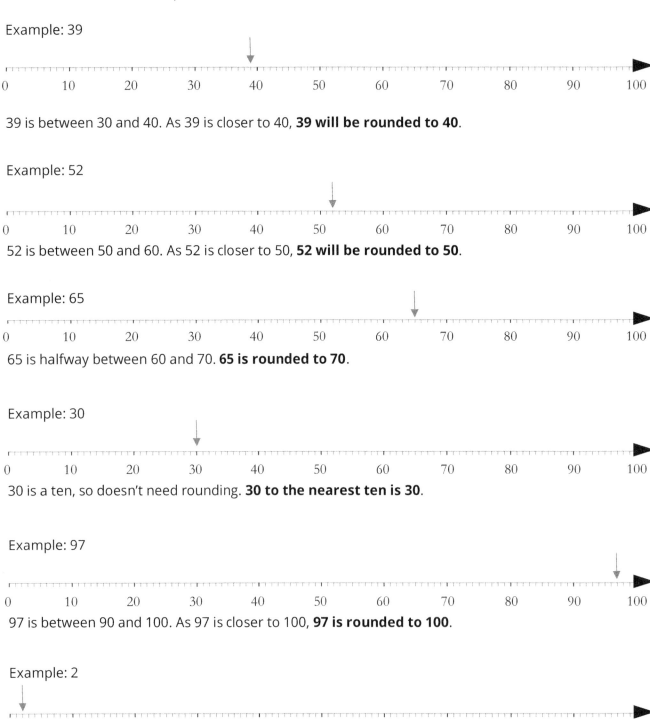

39 is between 30 and 40. As 39 is closer to 40, **39 will be rounded to 40**.

Example: 52

52 is between 50 and 60. As 52 is closer to 50, **52 will be rounded to 50**.

Example: 65

65 is halfway between 60 and 70. **65 is rounded to 70**.

Example: 30

30 is a ten, so doesn't need rounding. **30 to the nearest ten is 30**.

Example: 97

97 is between 90 and 100. As 97 is closer to 100, **97 is rounded to 100**.

Example: 2

2 is between 0 and 10. As 2 is closer to 0, **2 is rounded to 0**.

To round a number to the nearest ten, you look at the ones.
If the ones are **0**, **1**, **2**, **3** or **4**, you round the number **down**.
If the ones are **5**, **6**, **7**, **8** or **9**, you round the number **up**.
Example: 42 is rounded to 40. 85 is rounded to 90.

1 >Round these numbers to the nearest 10.

83 _____	19 _____	4 _____	27 _____	35 _____	50 _____
76 _____	54 _____	90 _____	99 _____	12 _____	75 _____
63 _____	71 _____	24 _____	68 _____	66 _____	5 _____

2 >Tanya bought a shirt for £27, a coat for £43 and an umbrella for £5. Use rounding to estimate the total cost of all three items.

_____

3 >Lana wants to exercise for 60 minutes this week. She has already done 38 minutes. Estimate how many more minutes she needs to exercise for.

_____

4 >Afzal works 17 hours a week. Estimate the number of hours he does in 4 weeks.

_____

5 >Luna needs 48 cupcakes for a party. There are 9 cupcakes in one box. Estimate how many boxes she needs to buy.

_____

6 >Check these calculations using estimation. The first one has been done for you. You can use a calculator.

43 + 38 =	64 – 18 =	11 + 57 =	93 – 3 =
Checking:	Checking:	Checking:	Checking:
40 + 40 = 80	_____	_____	_____
64 + 25 =	59 – 46 =	10 + 19 + 55 =	75 – 29 =
Checking:	Checking:	Checking:	Checking:
_____	_____	_____	_____

7 >Betty has £35. She wants to buy as many candles as possible. One candle costs £8.
Use estimation to work out how many candles betty can buy.

_____

8 > In a large pack there are 12 loo rolls. To work out how many loo rolls there are in 9 packs, Zen is doing this calculation: 12 x 9 = 108 Use estimation to check this answer.

_____

9 > A number has been rounded to the nearest ten. The rounded number is 20. What could the original number have been, before it was rounded?

_____, _____, _____, _____, _____, _____, _____, _____, _____, _____

10 > A number has been rounded to the nearest ten. The rounded number is 80. What could the original number have been, before it was rounded?

_____, _____, _____, _____, _____, _____, _____, _____, _____, _____

11 > A customer buys a coat for £44 and a pair of shoes for £38.
a) Calculate the total cost.

_____

b) Round the total to the nearest 10.

_____

12 > A mobile phone plan costs £8 per month, and Sam wants to pay for a full year in advance.
a) Round the monthly cost to the nearest 10.

_____

b) Estimate the annual cost.

_____

13 > Tom's electricity bill is £48, and his gas bill is £62 for the month. Estimate the total monthly expenses for electricity and gas.

_____

14 > In a charity event, two participants raised £59 and £74 each.
a) Calculate the total amount raised.

_____

b) Use estimation to check your answer to part a.

_____

Progress check

1. Fatima received these wages for the first two days of work last month:

   Day 1: £76 and **Day 2: £92**.

   a) How much did she get in total for both days?

   _____

   b) Check your answer using estimation.

   _____

2. Jade spent £81 the 1st week, £19 the 2nd week, and £55 the 3rd week.

   a) How much did she spend in total?

   _____

   b) Check your answer using estimation.

   _____

3. A number has been rounded to the nearest ten. The rounded number is 60. What could the original number have been, before it was rounded?

   _____, _____, _____, _____, _____, _____, _____, _____, _____, _____

4. Jade rounded 30 to the nearest 10. Here is her answer: 30. Is Jade correct? Explain your answer.

   _____

5. a) Round 43 to the nearest 10. _____

   b) Round 4 to the nearest 10. _____

   c) Round 95 to the nearest 10. _____

Recognise simple fractions (halves, quarters and tenths) of whole numbers and shapes

We use fractions when:
- ➢ sharing food
- ➢ cooking
- ➢ splitting the bill
- ➢ working with time
- ➢ Doing DIY activities

$$\frac{1}{4}$$

how many parts you are taking

how many parts there are in total

A fraction is part of a whole.

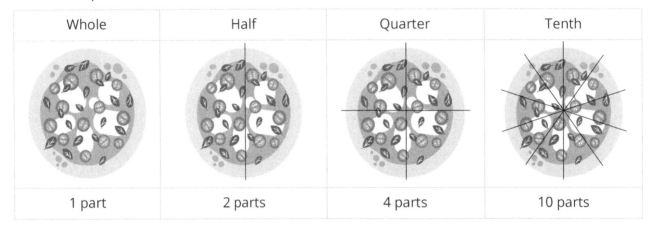

Whole	Half	Quarter	Tenth
1 part	2 parts	4 parts	10 parts

A half is written as $\frac{1}{2}$, which means 1 out of 2. It can also be shown as:

A quarter is written as $\frac{1}{4}$, which means 1 out of 4. It can also be shown as:

A tenth is written as $\frac{1}{10}$, which means 1 out of 10. It can also be shown as:

If we cut a pie into **two equal parts**, one of them is **a half**.

The pie can be cut in different ways, as long as it is split into two equal parts.

1 ⟩ Cut these shapes into halves.

   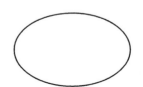 

2 a) Sue and her son are sharing this pizza.

Sue will take half of the pizza.
How many slices will Sue take?

_____

b) Steph has these sweets.

She is giving half of them to her friend.
How many sweets is Steph giving to her friend?

_____

c) Desi will use half of these eggs to make a cake.

How many eggs will Don use?

_____

d) Nike was given £10.

She will give half of the money to her brother.
How much will she keep?

_____

3 Lynn thinks she has cut this shape into halves.

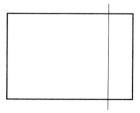

Is she correct? Why?

_____

| To work out half of a number, you divide the number by 2. |

4 Work out:

$\frac{1}{2}$ of 8	$\frac{1}{2}$ of 16	$\frac{1}{2}$ of 60	$\frac{1}{2}$ of 22	$\frac{1}{2}$ of 32
_____	_____	_____	_____	_____
$\frac{1}{2}$ of 10	$\frac{1}{2}$ of 2	$\frac{1}{2}$ of 100	$\frac{1}{2}$ of 18	$\frac{1}{2}$ of 200
_____	_____	_____	_____	_____
$\frac{1}{2}$ of 4	$\frac{1}{2}$ of 20	$\frac{1}{2}$ of 30	$\frac{1}{2}$ of 40	$\frac{1}{2}$ of 80
_____	_____	_____	_____	_____

If we cut a pie into **four equal parts**, one part is **a quarter** of the pie.

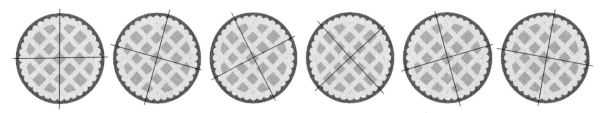

> The pie can be cut in different ways, as long as it is split into four equal parts.

5 > Cut these shapes into quarters.

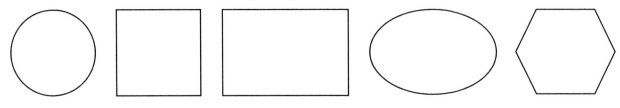

6 > Lynn thinks she has cut this shape into quarters.

Is she correct? Why?

_____

7 > a) Sue is sharing this pizza into quarters.

How many slices will there be in each quarter?

_____

b) Steph has 12 sweets.

She is giving a quarter of them to her friend. How many sweets is Steph giving to her friend?

_____

c) Jo is donating a quarter of these cans of tuna to a foodbank.

How many cans of tuna is Jo donating?

_____

d) Nike has £20.

She will give a quarter of the money to her friend. How much will she give to her friend?

_____

> To work out a quarter, you divide the number by 4.

8 Work out:

$\frac{1}{4}$ of 8	$\frac{1}{4}$ of 16	$\frac{1}{4}$ of 60	$\frac{1}{4}$ of 24	$\frac{1}{4}$ of 32
_____	_____	_____	_____	_____
$\frac{1}{4}$ of 10	$\frac{1}{4}$ of 40	$\frac{1}{4}$ of 100	$\frac{1}{4}$ of 12	$\frac{1}{4}$ of 200
_____	_____	_____	_____	_____
$\frac{1}{4}$ of 4	$\frac{1}{4}$ of 20	$\frac{1}{4}$ of 28	$\frac{1}{4}$ of 44	$\frac{1}{4}$ of 80
_____	_____	_____	_____	_____

9 Fill the gaps.

___ is $\frac{1}{2}$ of 36	4 is $\frac{1}{4}$ of 16	7 is $\frac{1}{2}$ of 14

A If we cut this pie into **ten equal parts**, one part is **a tenth** of the pie.

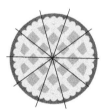

> The pie can be cut in different ways, as long as it is split into ten equal parts.

10 Cut these shapes into tenths.

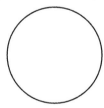  

11 Emma has a 100 cm long ribbon. She cuts off $\frac{1}{10}$ of the ribbon for her project. How long is the piece she cut off?

_____

12 a) Nike was given £20.

She will give a tenth of the money to her friend.
How much will she give to her friend?

_____

b) Steph has 40 sweets.

She is giving a tenth of them to her friend.
How many sweets is Steph giving to her friend?

_____

c) Don will have a tenth of these eggs for breakfast.

How many eggs will Don have for breakfast?

_____

d) Yee earns £120 a day. One tenth of that goes towards food.

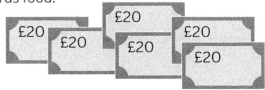

How much does Yee spend on food each day?

_____

To work out a tenth, you divide the number by 10.

13 Work out:

$\frac{1}{10}$ of 30	$\frac{1}{10}$ of 70	$\frac{1}{10}$ of 60	$\frac{1}{10}$ of 90
$\frac{1}{10}$ of 10	$\frac{1}{10}$ of 40	$\frac{1}{10}$ of 100	$\frac{1}{10}$ of 120
$\frac{1}{10}$ of 50	$\frac{1}{10}$ of 20	$\frac{1}{10}$ of 80	$\frac{1}{10}$ of 110

14 A book has 80 Pages. James reads $\frac{1}{4}$ of the book in one day. How many Pages does he read?

_____

15 Susan's garden has 60 flowers. She notices that $\frac{3}{4}$ of them are roses. How many roses are in her garden?

_____

16) a) Salma made 28 cupcakes for a party. When the party ended, only a quarter of the cupcakes were left.

How many cupcakes were left?

_____

b) Lola sells cheese.

This slice of cheese weighs 84g.
How much does half of it weigh?

_____

c) Naila made a cake and shared it with her family. She cut the cake into equal par

She gave her family 9 slices. One slice is left. What fraction of the cake is left?

_____

d) This is how many eggs Sonia has in the fridge.

Sonia uses $\frac{1}{10}$ of her eggs to make a cake.
How many eggs are left?

_____

17) What fraction of the whole do these represent?

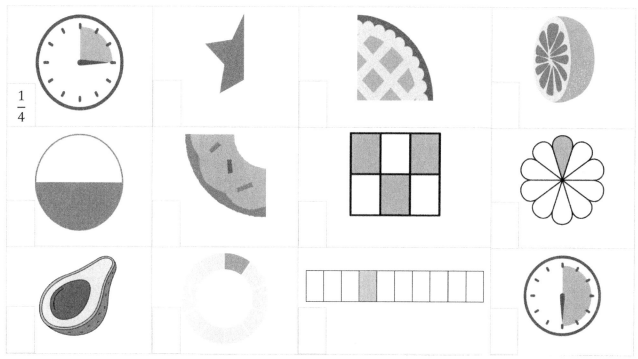

$\frac{1}{4}$

18) Hannah bought these tuna tins.

She thinks a quarter of these is equal to two tins. Is she correct?

_____

19 Roi says: 'To find a quarter of a number, you halve and halve the number again'. Is Roy correct?

_____

20 a) How many quarters are there in a half? _____

b) How many tenths are there in a half? _____

21 Colour in half of these bars.

22 Colour in a quarter of these rectangles.

23 Colour in a tenth of these rectangles.

24 a) Circle the fraction that represents the most.

$$\frac{1}{2} \qquad \frac{1}{10} \qquad \frac{1}{4}$$

b) Put the fractions in order, starting with the one that represents the most.

___   ___   ___

Progress check

1 Colour in $\frac{1}{10}$ of each shape below:

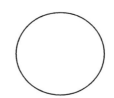

2 Jade represents $\frac{1}{4}$ like this:

Is she right? Explain your answer.

_____

3 Fill in the gaps.

Fraction in digits	Fraction in words
	one quarter
$\frac{1}{2}$	
	one tenth

4 Which of these is greater: $\frac{1}{2}$ of £64 **or** $\frac{1}{4}$ of £100?

_____

5 A shoe shop is selling shoes at a reduced price, $\frac{1}{2}$ off. The normal price of a pair of shoes is £30. How much do the shoes cost when they are on sale?

_____

6 Ayla says: '$\frac{1}{4}$ is bigger than $\frac{1}{2}$ because 4 is bigger than 2.' Is Ayla correct? Explain your answer.

_____

Read, write and use decimals to one decimal place

We use decimals when:
- ➤ working with money
- ➤ working with measures
- ➤ converting fractions into decimals
- ➤ working with time
- ➤ measuring body weight
- ➤ cooking

$\frac{1}{2}$ means 1 out of 2 . As a decimal, this is 0.5

We read this as **zero point five**.

$\frac{1}{10}$ means 1 out of 10. As a decimal, this is 0.1

We read this as **zero point one**.

1 Match the decimals in digits with how you say them in words.

| 3.4 | 16.7 | 0.9 | 10.0 | 140.3 |

| sixteen point seven | ten point zero | one hundred and forty point three | three point four | zero point nine |

Decimals have a **decimal point.**

Here is another example.

2	.	5
whole part		part of the whole

1	.	5
whole part		part of the whole

2 + 0.5 = 2.5

1+ 0.5 = 1.55

2 Fill the gaps.

| 7 + 0.6 = ___ | 10 + 0.6 = ___ | 23 + 0.9 = ___ | 0.1 + 14 = ___ | 99 + 0.2 = ___ | 101 + 0.7 = _____ |

Decimals represent part of a whole, just like fractions.

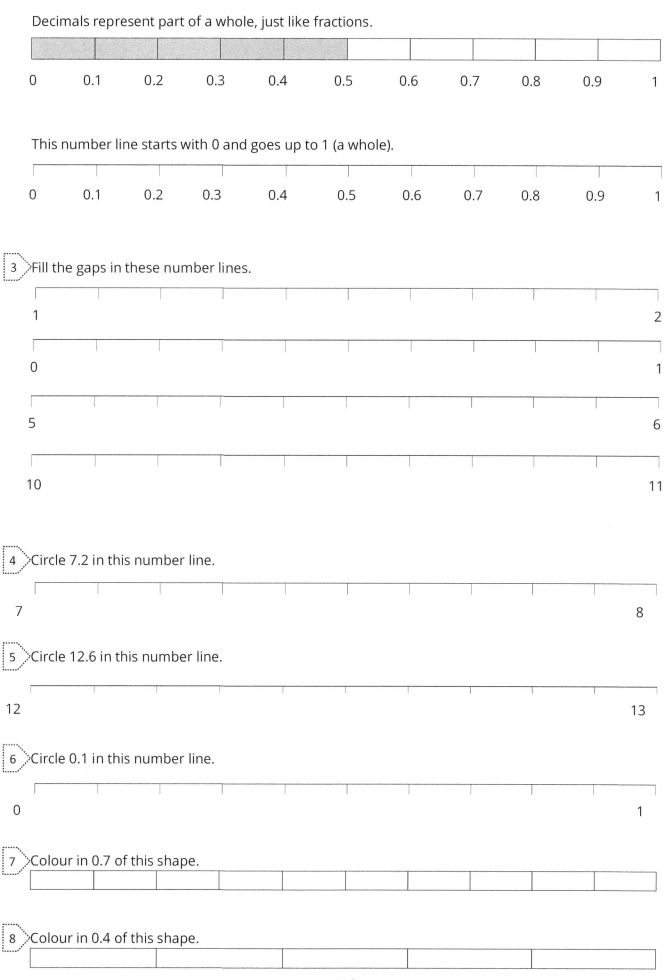

0   0.1   0.2   0.3   0.4   0.5   0.6   0.7   0.8   0.9   1

This number line starts with 0 and goes up to 1 (a whole).

0   0.1   0.2   0.3   0.4   0.5   0.6   0.7   0.8   0.9   1

3 Fill the gaps in these number lines.

1   2

0   1

5   6

10   11

4 Circle 7.2 in this number line.

7   8

5 Circle 12.6 in this number line.

12   13

6 Circle 0.1 in this number line.

0   1

7 Colour in 0.7 of this shape.

8 Colour in 0.4 of this shape.

Representing decimals

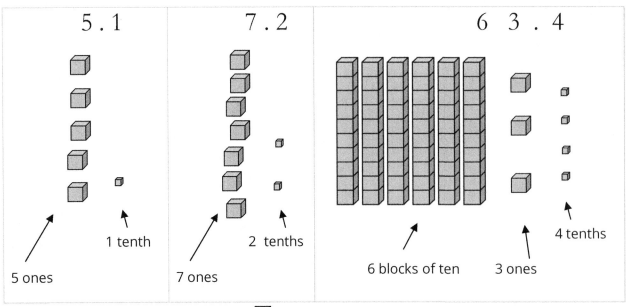

A **tenth** (◨) is 10 times smaller than 1 (▦).

9 ▷ Write down what decimals these represent. The first one has been done for you.

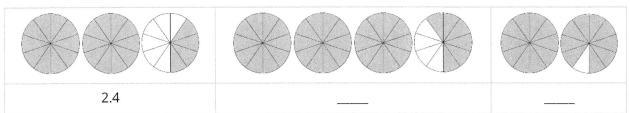

| 2.4 | _____ | _____ |

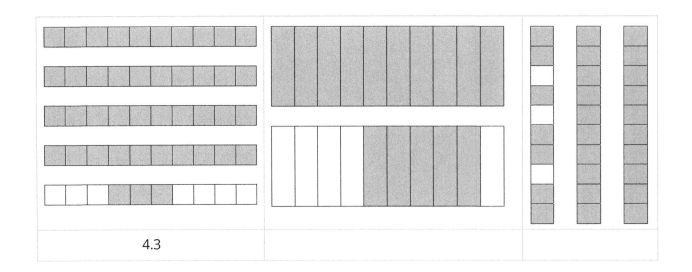

| 4.3 | | |

10 ▷ Colour in 0.2 of this shape.

Linking decimals with measurement

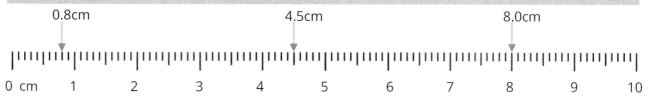

0.8cm   4.5cm   8.0cm

0 cm   1   2   3   4   5   6   7   8   9   10

11 Fill the gaps.

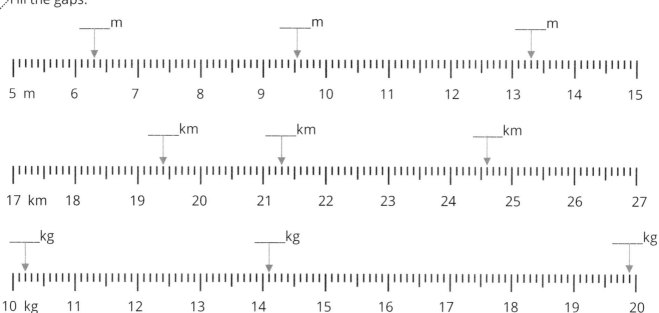

_____m   _____m   _____m

5 m   6   7   8   9   10   11   12   13   14   15

_____km   _____km   _____km

17 km   18   19   20   21   22   23   24   25   26   27

_____kg   _____kg   _____kg

10 kg   11   12   13   14   15   16   17   18   19   20

12 Read these scales.

_____   _____   _____

13 a) Circle the smallest number: 0.6   0.5   0.1

     b) Circle the smallest number: 0.9   0.3   1

     c) Circle the smallest number: 1.0   0.5   0.1

14 Put these numbers in order, starting with the smallest: 0.7   1.0   1.8   0.8

_____, _____, _____, _____

Adding decimals

+	2 . 5		+	0 . 8	
	3 . 2			5 . 1	
	5 . 7			5 . 9	

+	0 . 6		+	6 . 8	
	0 . 7			2 . 9	
	1 . 3			9 . 7	

15 Add these decimals.

3.1	2.4	5.6	5.0	1.3	1.3	1.4
+ 6.7	+ 6.5	+ 2.4	+ 3.7	+ 7.3	+ 8.6	+ 5.7

4.8	7.6	1.5	8.4	2.6	9.1	6.4
+ 4.1	+ 1.7	+ 7.2	+ 2.6	+ 7.7	+ 3.8	+ 7.4

Subtracting decimals

-	5 . 5		-	8 . 1	
	3 . 2			3 . 2	
	2 . 3			4 . 9	

-	1 . 5		-	2 . 3	
	0 . 8			1 . 9	
	0 . 7			0 . 4	

16 Subtract these decimals.

9.7	8.5	8.6	9.0	9.3	9.3	5.7
- 6.1	- 8.4	- 5.4	- 8.7	- 7.3	- 4.6	- 4.5

8.1	7.6	7.2	8.4	7.6	9.1	7.4
- 4.8	- 2.7	- 5.1	- 2.6	- 2.7	- 3.8	- 6.8

17 a) Luis is a postman. He is putting these boxes in order of weight, starting with the lightest.

A)10.6kg   B)2.4kg   C)1.9kg   D) 10.0kg

_____, _____, _____, _____

b) A bag of sugar weighs 1kg. A bag of flour weighs 1.5kg.
How much do they weigh altogether?

_____

c) Joss works in different offices each day. These are the distances to each office, from her house.

Monday **5.3km**

Tuesday **4.8km**

Wednesday **5.4km**

Thursday **5.0km**

Friday **4.6km**

Which office is the closest to her house?

_____

d) A water bottle holds 0.5 litres. How much do two bottles hold?

_____

e) Laura needs a new wardrobe. The space where the wardrobe will be put in, is 2.5m.

These are the lengths of the wardrobes Laura likes.

A	B	C	D
2.3m	2.0m	2.9m	2.6m

Laura wants the longest wardrobe that fits in the space. Which wardrobe should Laura buy?

_____

f) Ola has 0.8m of ribbon. She uses 0.5m to decorate a cake.

How much ribbon is left?

_____

18 Compare 1.2 and 2.1. Which is larger, and why?

_____

19 Jake fills his car with 34.7 litres of petrol. After driving for a while, the tank has 12.4 litres left. How many litres of petrol did Jake use?

_____

20 A recipe requires 2.3 litres of water, but John only has 1.7 litres. How much more water does he need to follow the recipe?

_____

Progress check

1 Colour in 0.5 of the bar below.

2 a) The length of a wood plank is 1.6 cm. What is the length of two planks of wood put next to each other?

_____

b) Would the two pieces put together be long enough to cover a strip of the floor that is 3m long?

_____

3 Fill in the gaps.

Decimal in digits	Decimal in words
	zero point six
4.9	
	ten point eight

4 What is the same about these two numbers and what is different?   3.7 and 7.3

_____

5 a) Here are three digit cards: 4   5   7
Make every decimal you can with them.

_____

b) Write them in order, starting with the smallest.

_____

Calculate money with pence up to one pound and in whole pounds of multiple items and write with correct symbols (£ and p)

We use money when:
- going shopping
- paying bills
- working out savings

These are the coins you should know.

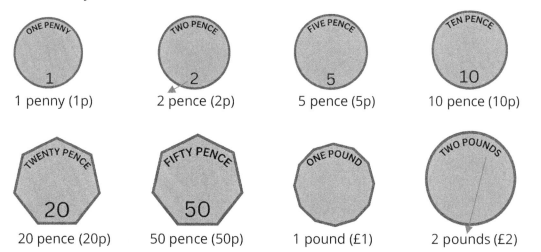

1 penny (1p)	2 pence (2p)	5 pence (5p)	10 pence (10p)
20 pence (20p)	50 pence (50p)	1 pound (£1)	2 pounds (£2)

These are the notes you should know.

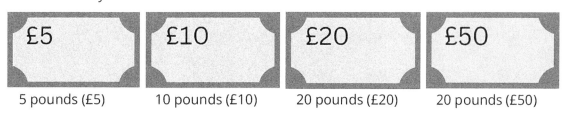

5 pounds (£5)	10 pounds (£10)	20 pounds (£20)	20 pounds (£50)

1 ▷ Match the coins with the value they have.

1p   2p   5p   £1   50p   20p   10p   £2

2 ▷ Draw these coins.

1p   2p   5p   £1   20p   10p   £2   50p

3 > Match notes with their values.

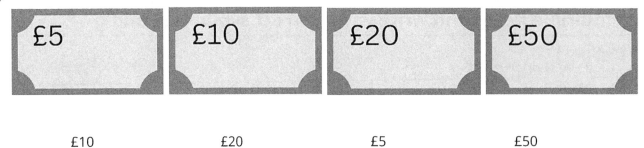

£10   £20   £5   £50

4 > Match the notations that mean the same amount.

1 penny   2 pounds   5 pence   10 pence   20 pounds   5 pounds   10 pounds   50 pence

5p   £2   £10   10p   £5   £20   1p   50p

5 > Draw the coin or note that has the same value as these.

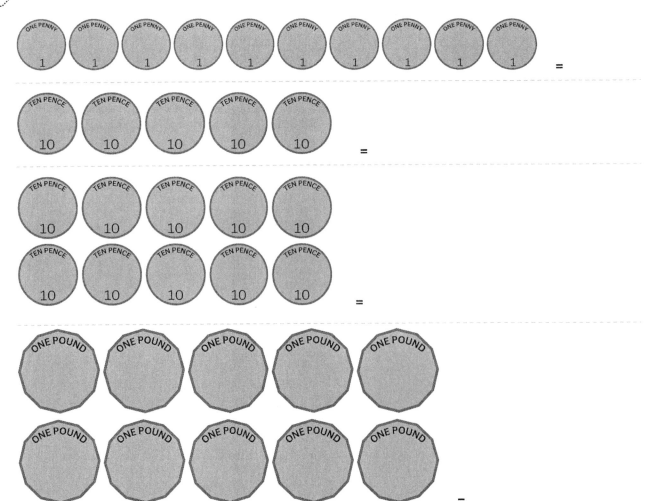

Adding and subtracting money

2	5	p	£	4	8		7	9	p	£	6	8
3	2	p	£	5	1		7	7	p	£	2	9
5	7	p	£	9	9			2	p	£	3	7

You can only add the same units: pounds only or pence only.

6 ▷ A protein bar costs 37p. Gary is buying two of them. Tick the coins he can pay with.

7 ▷ Cala is buying a jumper and a hat.
Tick the notes she can pay with.

£37

£23

£20	£50	£10	£5

8 ▷ Nita has put 100 of these coins in a coin machine. What will they be worth?

_____

9 ▷ These are coins that Ken has in a piggy bank.

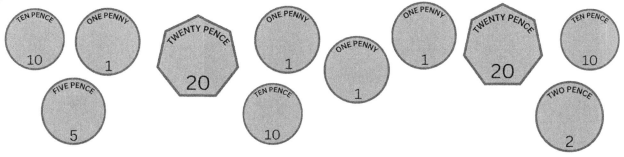

How much money does he have in his piggy bank? _____

10 ▷ Sukhdev is buying a turban for £18 and a pair of socks for £3.

a) How much do these items cost in total?
_____

b) He is paying with a £20 note and a £10 note. How much change will he get?
_____

11 ▷ a) Put 2p and 10p in the right places in this number line.

0   20p

b) Put £5 and £10 in the right places in this number line.

0   £20

12 ▷

a) Samira bought these items in a shop.	b) Lou thinks she needs to pay 37p.

a) Samira bought these items in a shop.

Cooking pot   **£18**
Frying pan   **£26**

How much did both items cost?

_____

Samira pays with a £50 note. How much change does she get?

_____

b) Lou thinks she needs to pay 37p.

RECEIPT

£37
TOTAL

Is she correct?

_____

c) Zara is paying for food in a restaurant. She writes **17£**. What is wrong with her answer?

_____

d) Dan is buying two shirts for £39 each. How much will he pay for both shirts?

_____

e) Jack is buying a shirt for £27 and a backpack for £19. He pays with this note.

£50

How much change will he get?

_____

f) Chris thinks this is a £50 note. Is he correct?

$50

_____

g) Chloe bought a pen for £3 and a notebook for £6. She thinks she has spent 9p. Is she right?

_____

h) Gent thinks he has spent £15p while shopping. What is wrong with **£15p**?

_____

Progress check

1 a) Match the coins with their values.

| 10p | 50p | 5p | £1 | 20p |

b) Put the values of the coins in order, from the lowest to the highest.

_____, _____, _____, _____, _____

2 You go to a shop and buy a pack of biscuits for 22p and 36p.

a) How much do they cost in total?

_____

b) You pay for the biscuits with a £1 coin. How much change do you get?

_____

c) Alan thinks you would get 52p change. Is he right? Explain your answer.

_____

3 Fill the gaps below. Include the unit.

| 19p + 43p = ___ | 66p – 34p = ___ | ___ + 72p = £1 |
| 35p + ___ = £1 | 79p – ___ = 69p | £1 – 58p = ___ |

4 Gurpreet lines up the cost of two different items to add them up. Here is what she has done:

$$\begin{array}{r} 56\text{p} \\ +\ 29\text{p} \\ \hline \end{array}$$

Is this correct? Explain your answer.

_____

5 a) Match the notes below with their values.

| £5 | £10 | £20 | £50 |

£20   £50   £5   £10

b) Put the values of the notes in order, from the highest to the lowest.

_____, _____, _____, _____

6 You go to a shop and buy three items as shown below.

Sale!!!
Chairs £58
Table £79

a) How much would one table and two chairs cost in total?

_____

b) In another shop, the same table and chairs are sold as a set for £180. What is the difference in price?

_____

7 Fill the gaps below. Include the unit.

| £19 + £43 = ___ | £35 + ___ = £100 | £79 – ___ = £69 | £66 – £34 = ___ |

8 Gurpreet lines up the cost of two different items to add them up. Here is what she has done:
Is this correct? Explain your answer.

£56
+ 29p
‾‾‾‾‾‾

_____

9 Order these amounts, starting with the lowest in value.

5p   2p   £10   10p   £5   £20   1p   50p

_____,   _____,   _____,   _____,   _____,   _____,   _____,   _____

Know the number of hours in a day and weeks in a year. Be able to name and sequence them

We use the number of hours in a day or weeks in a year, when:
- ➢ planning shopping trips
- ➢ planning holidays
- ➢ working out pay per year
- ➢ planning projects
- ➢ making appointments
- ➢ taking medication

Know the number of hours in a day. Be able to name and sequence them

There are 24 hours in a day. The day starts at 12 middnight and finishes at 12 midnight.

Hours go like this:

00:00 Midnight	01:00	02:00	03:00	04:00	05:00	06:00	07:00	08:00	09:00	10:00	11:00
12:00 Midday	13:00	14:00	15:00	16:00	17:00	18:00	19:00	20:00	21:00	22:00	23:00

At this time, you're probably sleeping:	At this time, you're probably having lunch:

This is the midnight.	This is the midday.

1. Oil paint takes one day to dry fully. How many hours does the paint take to dry?

_____

2. Nas is off-sick at home. He has been told to return to school after 48 hours.
   After how many days should Nas return to school?

_____

3. Calculate the total number of hours in 3 days.

_____

4. a) If it is 5:00 in the morning, how many hours are left until midday? _____
   b) If it is 7:00 in the evening, how many hours are left until midnight? _____

5. Dora thinks 12pm is 12 midnight. Is she correct?

_____

There are 52 weeks in a year.

This is the 1st week of the year 2022

January

Sun	Mon	Tue	Wed	Thu	Fri	Sat
1	2	3	4	5	6	7
8	9	10	11	12	13	14
15	16	17	18	19	20	21
22	23	24	25	26	27	28
29	30	31				

February

Sun	Mon	Tue	Wed	Thu	Fri	Sat
			1	2	3	4
5	6	7	8	9	10	11
12	13	14	15	16	17	18
19	20	21	22	23	24	25
26	27	28				

March

Sun	Mon	Tue	Wed	Thu	Fri	Sat
			1	2	3	4
5	6	7	8	9	10	11
12	13	14	15	16	17	18
19	20	21	22	23	24	25
26	27	28	29	30	31	

This is the 14th week of the year 2022

April

Sun	Mon	Tue	Wed	Thu	Fri	Sat
						1
2	3	4	5	6	7	8
9	10	11	12	13	14	15
16	17	18	19	20	21	22
23	24	25	26	27	28	29
30						

May

Sun	Mon	Tue	Wed	Thu	Fri	Sat
	1	2	3	4	5	6
7	8	9	10	11	12	13
14	15	16	17	18	19	20
21	22	23	24	25	26	27
28	29	30	31			

June

Sun	Mon	Tue	Wed	Thu	Fri	Sat
				1	2	3
4	5	6	7	8	9	10
11	12	13	14	15	16	17
18	19	20	21	22	23	24
25	26	27	28	29	30	

July

Sun	Mon	Tue	Wed	Thu	Fri	Sat
						1
2	3	4	5	6	7	8
9	10	11	12	13	14	15
16	17	18	19	20	21	22
23	24	25	26	27	28	29
30	31					

August

Sun	Mon	Tue	Wed	Thu	Fri	Sat
		1	2	3	4	5
6	7	8	9	10	11	12
13	14	15	16	17	18	19
20	21	22	23	24	25	26
27	28	29	30	31		

September

Sun	Mon	Tue	Wed	Thu	Fri	Sat
					1	2
3	4	5	6	7	8	9
10	11	12	13	14	15	16
17	18	19	20	21	22	23
24	25	26	27	28	29	30

October

Sun	Mon	Tue	Wed	Thu	Fri	Sat
1	2	3	4	5	6	7
8	9	10	11	12	13	14
15	16	17	18	19	20	21
22	23	24	25	26	27	28
29	30	31				

November

Sun	Mon	Tue	Wed	Thu	Fri	Sat
		1	2	3	4	
5	6	7	8	9	10	11
12	13	14	15	16	17	18
19	20	21	22	23	24	25
26	27	28	29	30		

December

Sun	Mon	Tue	Wed	Thu	Fri	Sat
					1	2
3	4	5	6	7	8	9
10	11	12	13	14	15	16
17	18	19	20	21	22	23
24	25	26	27	28	29	30
31						

This is the 52nd week of the year

6 ▷ A shop is closed in the last week of the year. Which month does that week fall on.

_____

7 ▷ Jana starts a course in the first week of the new year. Which month does that fall on?

_____

8 ▷ Tanya has 6 weeks annual leave each year. How many weeks does Tanya work each year?

_____

9 ▷ A supermarket is closed every Sunday. The rest of the days, the supermarket is open. How many days is the supermarket closed for in a year?

_____

10) How many weeks are there in two years? _____

11) Lola is getting married in exactly six months from now. How many weeks is it until then?
_____

12) Kirsty thinks there are 60 hours in a day. Is she correct?
_____

13) Drake says 'If there are four weeks in each month, there must be 48 weeks in a year. Is he correct?
_____

14) Sona works part time. She works two days a week, all year around. How many days does she work in a year?
_____

Progress check

1) How many weeks are there in one year? _____

2) How many hours are there in a day? _____

3) At what time does a new day start? _____

4) At what time does a day end? _____

5) How many months are there in a year? _____

6) Which month is the first week of the year in? _____

7) Sara is starting a new course.

a) The course takes place for 36 weeks in a year. How many weeks will Sara be off in a year?
_____

b) The course will last three years. How many weeks will Sara be attending in total?
_____

8) It is the 11th week of the year. How many weeks are left until the end of the year?
_____

Read and record time in common date formats, and read time displayed on analogue clocks in hours, half hours and quarter hours, and understand hours from a 24-hour digital clock

We need to know how to read time and write date, so that we:
- ➢ can plan our time
- ➢ get to events on time
- ➢ work out how long an event takes
- ➢ go to work, school or college on time
- ➢ plan holidays
- ➢ take the bus or train
- ➢ don't burn food in the oven
- ➢ go to appointments on time

Read and record time in common date formats

Here is an example of how to write the date: 16th January 2023

the ↗

January						2023
Mon	Tue	Wed	Thu	Fri	Sat	Sun
						1
2	3	4	5	6	7	8
9	10	11	12	13	14	15
16	17	18	19	20	21	22
23	24	25	26	27	28	29
30	31					

the ↗

← the year

Date is written as **day – month – year**.

The date is 16th January 2023. We read this as 'twenty-fifth of January twenty twenty-three'.

These are some more examples of how to read dates.

1st April 1984	2nd June 1946	3rd December 2005
first of April	second of June	third of December
nineteen eighty-four	nineteen forty-six	two thousand and five

1 ▷ Circle these dates on the calendars.

August						
Mon	Tue	Wed	Thu	Fri	Sat	Sun
1	2	3	4	5	6	7
8	9	10	11	12	13	14
15	16	17	18	19	20	21
22	23	24	25	26	27	28
29	30	31				

eighth of August

February						
Mon	Tue	Wed	Thu	Fri	Sat	Sun
		1	2	3	4	5
6	7	8	9	10	11	12
13	14	15	16	17	18	19
20	21	22	23	24	25	26
27	28					

thirteenth of February

December						
Mon	Tue	Wed	Thu	Fri	Sat	Sun
				1	2	3
4	5	6	7	8	9	10
11	12	13	14	15	16	17
18	19	20	21	22	23	24
25	26	27	28	29	30	31

twenty-seventh of December

June						
Mon	Tue	Wed	Thu	Fri	Sat	Sun
			1	2	3	4
5	6	7	8	9	10	11
12	13	14	15	16	17	18
19	20	21	22	23	24	25
26	27	28	29	30		

second of June

2) Write the date each calendar shows. The first one has been done for you.

March						2023
Mon	Tue	Wed	Thu	Fri	Sat	Sun
		1	2	3	4	5
6	7	8	9	(10)	11	12
13	14	15	16	17	18	19
20	21	22	23	24	25	26
27	28	29	30	31		

_____10th March 2023_____

September						2007
Mon	Tue	Wed	Thu	Fri	Sat	Sun
					1	2
3	4	5	6	7	8	9
10	11	12	13	14	15	16
17	18	(19)	20	21	22	23
24	25	26	27	28	29	30

_____

November						2011
Mon	Tue	Wed	Thu	Fri	Sat	Sun
	1	(2)	3	4	5	6
7	8	9	10	11	12	13
14	15	16	17	18	19	20
21	22	23	24	25	26	27
28	29	30				

_____

April						1995
Mon	Tue	Wed	Thu	Fri	Sat	Sun
					1	2
3	4	5	6	7	8	9
10	11	12	13	14	15	16
17	18	19	20	21	(22)	23
24	25	26	27	28	29	30

_____

October						1976
Mon	Tue	Wed	Thu	Fri	Sat	Sun
				1	2	3
4	5	6	7	8	9	10
11	12	(13)	14	15	16	17
18	19	20	21	22	23	24
25	26	27	28	29	30	31

_____

July						1963
Mon	Tue	Wed	Thu	Fri	Sat	Sun
1	2	3	4	5	6	7
8	9	10	11	12	13	14
15	16	17	18	19	20	21
22	23	24	25	26	27	28
29	(30)					

_____

May						2025
Mon	Tue	Wed	Thu	Fri	Sat	Sun
			1	2	3	4
5	6	7	8	9	10	11
12	13	14	15	16	(17)	18
19	20	21	22	23	24	25
26	27	28	29	30		

_____

August						2027
Mon	Tue	Wed	Thu	Fri	Sat	Sun
						1
2	3	4	5	6	7	8
9	10	11	12	13	14	15
16	17	18	19	20	21	22
(23)	24	25	26	27	28	29
30	31					

_____

These are examples of how to write the same date:

17 June 2022   17th June 2022   17.06.2022   17.06.22

3) Write these dates in three different ways:

May						2025
Mon	Tue	Wed	Thu	Fri	Sat	Sun
			1	2	3	4
5	6	7	(8)	9	10	11
12	13	14	15	16	17	18
19	20	21	22	23	24	25
26	27	28	29	30		

_____, _____, _____

August						2027
Mon	Tue	Wed	Thu	Fri	Sat	Sun
						1
2	3	4	5	6	7	8
9	10	11	12	13	14	15
16	17	18	19	(20)	21	22
23	24	25	26	27	28	29

_____, _____, _____

Look at this yearly calendar for 2023.

January

Sun	Mon	Tue	Wed	Thu	Fri	Sat
1	2	3	4	5	6	7
8	9	10	11	12	13	14
15	16	17	18	19	20	21
22	23	24	25	26	27	28
29	30	31				

February

Sun	Mon	Tue	Wed	Thu	Fri	Sat
			1	2	3	4
5	6	7	8	9	10	11
12	13	14	15	16	17	18
19	20	21	22	23	24	25
26	27	28				

March

Sun	Mon	Tue	Wed	Thu	Fri	Sat
			1	2	3	4
5	6	7	8	9	10	11
12	13	14	15	16	17	18
19	20	21	22	23	24	25
26	27	28	29	30	31	

April

Sun	Mon	Tue	Wed	Thu	Fri	Sat
						1
2	3	4	5	6	7	8
9	10	11	12	13	14	15
16	17	18	19	20	21	22
23	24	25	26	27	28	29
30						

May

Sun	Mon	Tue	Wed	Thu	Fri	Sat
	1	2	3	4	5	6
7	8	9	10	11	12	13
14	15	16	17	18	19	20
21	22	23	24	25	26	27
28	29	30	31			

June

Sun	Mon	Tue	Wed	Thu	Fri	Sat
				1	2	3
4	5	6	7	8	9	10
11	12	13	14	15	16	17
18	19	20	21	22	23	24
25	26	27	28	29	30	

July

Sun	Mon	Tue	Wed	Thu	Fri	Sat
						1
2	3	4	5	6	7	8
9	10	11	12	13	14	15
16	17	18	19	20	21	22
23	24	25	26	27	28	29
30	31					

August

Sun	Mon	Tue	Wed	Thu	Fri	Sat
		1	2	3	4	5
6	7	8	9	10	11	12
13	14	15	16	17	18	19
20	21	22	23	24	25	26
27	28	29	30	31		

September

Sun	Mon	Tue	Wed	Thu	Fri	Sat
					1	2
3	4	5	6	7	8	9
10	11	12	13	14	15	16
17	18	19	20	21	22	23
24	25	26	27	28	29	30

October

Sun	Mon	Tue	Wed	Thu	Fri	Sat
1	2	3	4	5	6	7
8	9	10	11	12	13	14
15	16	17	18	19	20	21
22	23	24	25	26	27	28
29	30	31				

November

Sun	Mon	Tue	Wed	Thu	Fri	Sat
			1	2	3	4
5	6	7	8	9	10	11
12	13	14	15	16	17	18
19	20	21	22	23	24	25
26	27	28	29	30		

December

Sun	Mon	Tue	Wed	Thu	Fri	Sat
					1	2
3	4	5	6	7	8	9
10	11	12	13	14	15	16
17	18	19	20	21	22	23
24	25	26	27	28	29	30
31						

a) What day is 13th May?

_____

b) What day is 23rd November?

_____

c) What day is 7th March?

_____

d) What day is 17th June?

_____

e) What day is 25th December?

_____

f) What day is 31st July?

_____

g) What day is 3rd January?

_____

h) What day is 23rd October?

_____

February usually has 28 days. Every four years, February has 29 days. The other months of the year have either 30 days or 31 days. You can use your knuckles to work out how many days a month has.

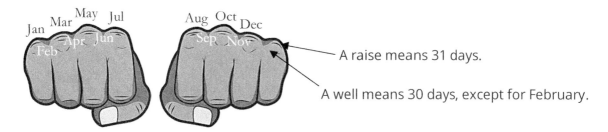

A raise means 31 days.

A well means 30 days, except for February.

5 How many days are there in April? _____

6 How many days are there in October? _____

In the American format, date is written as month – day – year
11 March 2023 is written as 03.11.23

7 a) This is the day when Desi started her course.

June

Mon	Tue	Wed	Thu	Fri	Sat	Sun
			1	2	3	4
5	6	7	8	(9)	10	11
12	13	14	15	16	17	18
19	20	21	22	23	24	25
26	27	28	29	30		

Three months after, she started another course. On what date did she start the other course?
_____

b) On this day it was Jack's birthday. He turned 38.

June   2022

Mon	Tue	Wed	Thu	Fri	Sat	Sun
			1	2	3	4
5	6	7	8	9	10	11
12	(13)	14	15	16	17	18
19	20	21	22	23	24	25
26	27	28	29	30		

On what date did Jack turn 37?
_____

c) In Lee's Laptop, the date is shown in American format. This is the date shown: 02/08/2023

What month is this in?
_____

d) Sona ordered two sofas on 16th January. They will be delivered in 14 days.

When will the sofas be delivered?
_____

e) Keith is due a gas check on his property. These are the dates he could have the gas check on:

15.06.23	23.06.23	18.06.23	28.06.23

He's going on holiday from the 10th June to the 25th June. Circle the dates he can have the gas check on.

f) Graham reading a book with historical facts. He reads this date: 31.01.20

He thinks this is 31st January 1920. Is he correct? Why?
_____

In the analogue clock:

We have two clock types:

analogue clock

digital clock

The long hand tells the minutes

The short hand tells the hours

This clock shows it's 4 o'clock or 4:00

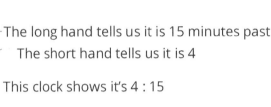

The long hand tells us it is 15 minutes past

The short hand tells us it is 4

This clock shows it's 4 : 15

The short hand tells us it is 4

The long hand tells us it is 30 minutes past

This clock shows 4 : 30

The long hand tells us it is 45 minutes past

The short hand tells us it is 4

This clock shows 4 : 45

| 1 hour = 60 mins | $\frac{1}{2}$ hour = 15 mins | $\frac{1}{4}$ hour = 30 mins | $\frac{3}{4}$ hour = 45 mins |

Write the time under each clock.

_____   _____   _____   _____

9 Match the clocks with the correct time.

12 : 15   1 : 15   5 : 15   10 : 15

10 Write the time under each clock.

_____   _____   _____   _____

11 Match the clocks with the correct time.

2 : 30   12 : 30   3 : 30   5 : 30

12 > Write the time under each clock.

_____   _____   _____   _____

13 > Match the clocks with the correct time.

1 : 45   7 : 45   3 : 45   5 : 45

14 > Write the time under each clock.

_____   _____   _____   _____

15 > Andy will go out between 2 : 45 and 4 : 30. Tick the clock that shows this time.

16 > Draw clock that show these times.

11 : 30   6 : 15   8 : 45   5 : 30

1 : 00   12 : 15   10 : 45   9 : 15

17 > Dan goes to work after 8 : 15.

Tick the clock that shows a time after 8 : 15.

18 > a) Ian thinks this clock shows it's quarter to four.

b) Ian thinks this clock shows it's quarter to three.

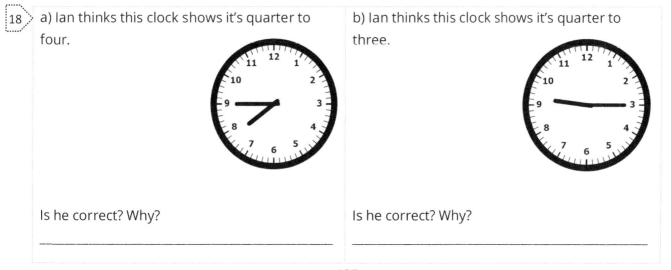

Is he correct? Why?
_____

Is he correct? Why?
_____

There are different ways to read time.

ten thirty	twelve fifteen	three forty five
half past ten	quarter past twelve	forty five past three
		quarter to four

19 Circle all the correct ways you can read this time in: 9 : 45.

| quarter past nine | quarter past ten | quarter to ten | forty-five past nine | nine forty-five |

20 Circle all the correct ways you can read this time in: 11 : 15.

| quarter past eleven | half past eleven | quarter to eleven | fifteen past eleven | eleven fifteen |

21 Circle all the correct ways you can read this time in: 12 : 30.

| quarter past twelve | half past eleven | thirty past twelve | twelve thirty | forty five past twelve |

22 Neil is getting ready for an interview. He leaves the house at quarter past eight. He then travels by bus for 30 minutes. At what time does he arrive at the interview?

_____

23 Donna is going to the city centre by train. The train arrives in the city centre at 11:30.

The train journey takes 15 minutes. What time does the train depart?

_____

24 James arrives at the gym at 7:45 in the morning. His workout session lasts 1 hour and 15 minutes. At what time does he finish his workout session? Show your working out.

_____

Understand hours from a 24-hour digital clock

In a digital clock:

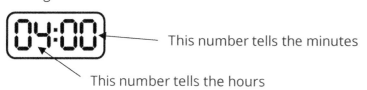

This number tells the minutes

This number tells the hours

This digital clock shows it's 4 o'clock:

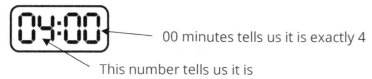

00 minutes tells us it is exactly 4

This number tells us it is

The hours in a digital clock are read as:

7 **hundred hours** (07:00)

12 **hundred hours** (12:00)

14 **hundred hours** (14:00)

These are a few more examples.

| 7 o'clock | 12 o'clock | 8 o'clock | 3 o'clock | 1 o'clock |

Hours go like this:

morning

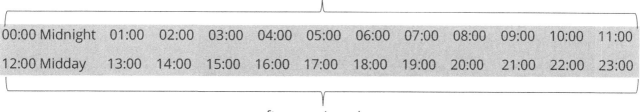

| 00:00 Midnight | 01:00 | 02:00 | 03:00 | 04:00 | 05:00 | 06:00 | 07:00 | 08:00 | 09:00 | 10:00 | 11:00 |
| 12:00 Midday | 13:00 | 14:00 | 15:00 | 16:00 | 17:00 | 18:00 | 19:00 | 20:00 | 21:00 | 22:00 | 23:00 |

afternoon/evening

Examples:

13:00 is 1 o'clock in the afternoon. We work this out, we do: 13 – 12 = 1
20:00 is 8 o'clock in the evening. We work this out, we do: 20 – 12 = 8
6 o'clock in the evening is written as 18:00. We work this out, we do: 6 + 12 = 18
2 o'clock in the afternoon is written as 14:00. We work this out, we do: 2 + 12 = 14

These are a few more examples of time in the afternoon and evening.

   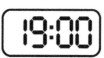 

| 3 o'clock | 12 o'clock | 4 o'clock | 7 o'clock | 10 o'clock |

25 Write the time under each clock.

   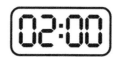 

_____ _____ _____ _____ _____

26 > Write the time under each clock.

 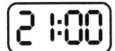   

_____ _____ _____ _____ _____

27 > Match the clocks that show the same time.

28 > Jocelyn is going to meet a friend at ten in the morning. Tick the clock that shows the time she will meet her friend.

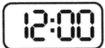  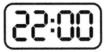 

29 > Stacey is going for a job interview at two o'clock in the afternoon. Tick the clock that shows the time she has the interview in.

 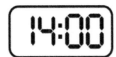  

30 > Safiya is going to a party at 8 in the evening. Tick the clock that shows the time she is going to the party.

31 > Sandra's work shift starts at 9:30 in the morning and ends at 2:30 in the afternoon. How many hours does she work? Show your working out.

_____

138

a) Chris is getting ready to go to college. He leaves the house at half past seven. This is the time now.

Is it time to go to leave the house? Explain your answer.

_____

b) These are the opening times of a shop.

Mon 10:00 – 14:00

Tue 10:00 – 15:00

Wed 10:00 – 15:00

Thu 10:00 – 15:00

Fri 10:00 – 14:00

How many hours is the shop open for on Wednesday?

_____

c) Sonia is getting ready to go to a party. She will leave in three hours. This is the time now.

When will Sonia leave?

_____

e) Van came back from college 3 hours ago. This is the time now.

When did Van come back from college?

_____

d) Lorna goes to sleep at this time in the evening:

She then wakes up at this time in the morning:

06:00

How many hours has she slept for?

_____

f) Kate starts cooking dinner at 6:15 in the evening. The recipe states that the dish takes 45 minutes to prepare. What time will the dish be ready?

_____

g) Sophie's train arrives at 10:45 in the morning and then she does a 30-minute walk to work. What time will she arrive at work?

_____

h) Suny thinks there are 100 minutes in one hour. Is he correct? Explain your answer.

_____

i) How many quarter hours are there in half an hour?

_____

j) A museum is open from 10:00 in the morning to 4:30 in the afternoon. How many hours is the museum open per day?

_____

k) Lisa's online class starts at 6:30 in the evening and lasts for 2.5 hours. When does the class finish?

_____

Progress check

1. Sumra was born on 19.10.80.
   a) Which month was Sumra born in?_____ b) Which year was Sumra born in?_____

2. Write this date in three different date formats: 17 February 2023 _____, _____, _____

3. Write the time under each clock.

_____   _____   _____   _____

4. Write the time under each clock.

 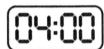   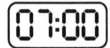

___11 o'clock___   _____   _____   _____   _____

5. Show 'quarter to 10' in the clock face.

6. Zen writes the 2nd April 2020 as : 04.02.2020 Is he correct? Explain your answer.

_____

7. A webinar starts at 3:30 in the afternoon and ends two and a half hours later. When does the webinar end? Show your working out.

_____

8. Jasmine has an 8-hour shift at work. She starts at 9:00 am. At what time does her shift end? Show your working out.

_____

Use metric measures of length including millimetres, centimetres, metres and kilometres

We use millimetres, centimetres, metres and kilometres to measure:
- ➢ the length or width of furniture
- ➢ the distance between places
- ➢ the length of fabric
- ➢ the height of people

We use these instruments to measure length:

measuring tape or tape measure   ruler

To measure, you align the ruler or measuring tape with the item you are measuring.

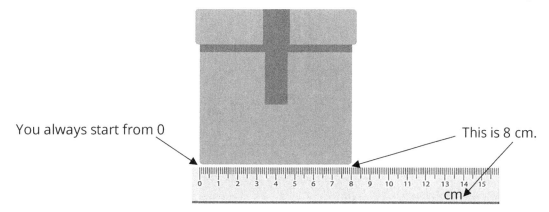

You always start from 0   This is 8 cm.

1 ⟩ Measure these lines using a ruler.

——————————————————————   ___ cm

———————————————————————————   ___ cm

——————————————   ___ cm

———————————————————————————————   ___ cm

———————————————————   ___ cm

—————————————————————————————————————   ___ cm

—————————————————————————————   ___ cm

————————————————————————————————   ___ cm

2 > How wide is this picture frame? Don't forget to add the unit in your answer.

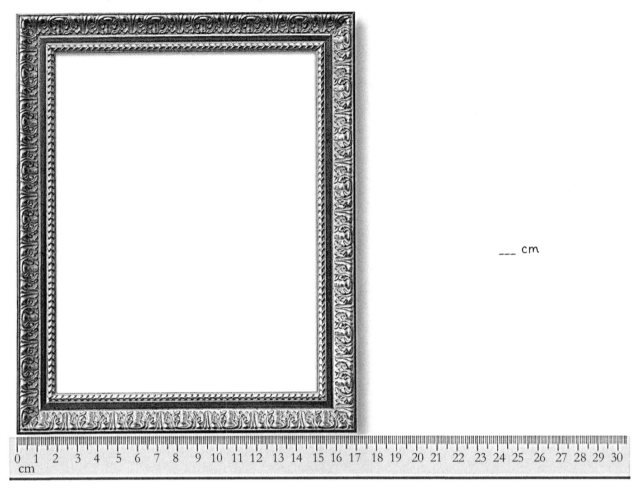

___ cm

3 > Which of these is the longest? Circle your answer.

14cm   85cm   72cm   49cm

4 > Put these suitcases in order of width, starting with the narrowest.

62cm   59cm   60cm   63cm

_____, _____, _____, _____

5 > Circle the shortest measurement:

0.5m   1m   0.7m   1.2m

In a ruler, you will usually see millimetres (mm) and centimetres (cm). This ruler measures up to 30cm.

The small divisions represent millimeters.
Can you count how many millimetres there are in one centimetre?

There are 10mm in 1cm.
The width of a nail is about 1cm.   The depth of a finger nail is about 1mm.

6 Jeta is posting a package. The maximum length the box can have is 18cm. She wants to use the longest box for posting.

15.5cm   19cm   16.2cm

Which of the boxes will Jeta use?

_____

7 Zain needs a 60mm wire. These are the options:

    55mm   70mm   45mm   40mm

Which of them should Zain buy? Why?

_____

8 John has 4 planks of wood in different lengths:
    a) 2.2 meters   b) 1.7 meters   c) 2.5 meters   d) 1.9 meters

Which plank is closest to 2 meters long? _____

9 Gela is shopping for a lamp shade. These are the ones she likes. Gela wants to buy the shortest one.

    1.5m   1.8m   2.0m   1.6m

Tick the lamp shade Gela should buy.

To measure the distance between places, we use kilometres (km). A measuring tape is very similar to a ruler, only longer. You will see cm, mm and m in a measuring tape.

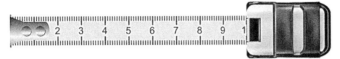

The small divisions represent millimetres. The bigger divisions

100cm = 1m
Centi, like **cent** or **century**, means 100.
That's why 100cm in 1m.
The span between shoulder and the fingers on the other hand, is about 1 metre.

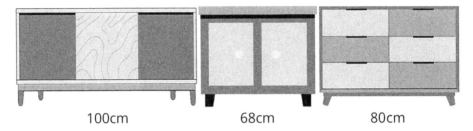

10. Zain needs a new storage cabinet. The space where he will put the cabinet is 85cm long. These are the cabinets that Zain likes.

| 100cm | 68cm | 80cm |

He wants to buy the longest cabinet that fits the space. Tick the cabinet Zain should buy.

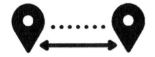

Kilometres are much longer than metres. We use kilometres to measure long

11. Write the short form of each unit.

kilometre   millimetre   metre   centimetre

_____   _____   _____   _____

12. Put these units in order, starting with the shortest.

kilometre   Millimetre   metre   centimetre

_____, _____, _____, _____

13. Lora is planning to visit four different towns in the next few weeks. She will visit them in order of distance, starting with the shortest.

Town A   **Town B**   **Town C**   **Town D**
73.5km   70.2km   68.9km   74.0km

Put the towns in the order that Lora will visit them. _____, _____, _____, _____

14. Lisa walks from her house to the library, which is 1.3 kilometers away. Then she walks to the grocery store, which is another 0.7 kilometers away. How far does she walk in total?

_____

15 > Cala works in different offices each day. These are the distances of each office from her home.

6.2km   8.9km   10.1km   7.5km

Put these distances in order, starting with the shortest: _____, _____, _____, _____

16 > Noor lives 3.7km away from her sister. She is visiting her sister today and returning tomorrow. What is the total distance Noor is travelling? Include the unit in your answer.

_____

17 > A footpath is 11.8 kilometers long. If you walk half the distance, how many kilometers do you walk? You can use a calculator to work this out.

_____

18 > Tick the correct option.

a) The height of a tree is about:

3mm   3cm   3m   3km

b) The length of an earring is about:

2mm   2cm   2m   2km

c) The depth of this package that fits in the letterbox is about:

20mm   20cm   20m   20km

d) The height of a toddler is about:

80mm   80cm   80m   80km

19 > Sara thinks the distance between town A and town B is 20m. What is wrong with her answer?

_____

20 > Lou says the height of a tree in her front garden is "2 meters long". What is wrong with her answer?

_____

21 > Charles thinks 4.0km is the same as 4km. Is he correct?

_____

22 > A swimming pool has a depth of 1.2 meters at the shallow end and 2.0 meters at the deep end. How much deeper is the deep end compared to the shallow end?

_____

Progress check

1 > Fill in the gaps below.

The short form of writing **millimetre** is _____ . The short form of writing **kilometre** is _____
The short form of writing _____ is **m**. The short form of writing _____ is **cm**.

2 > Ayan is measuring his height.

What is Ayan's height in centimetres? _____

3 > Put these measurements in order, from the smallest to the largest: 1 cm, 1 m, 1 mm and 1 km.

_____, _____, _____, _____

4 > How long is the blue line below? Include the unit.

5 > Sumra wants to buy two bookcases, each 46cm long. She wants to put them next to each other in her bedroom. How much space would both bookcases take in total?

_____

146

Use metric measures of weight including grams and kilograms

We measure the weight of:
  ➤ ingredients when cooking
  ➤ parcels when posting
  ➤ groceries when shopping
  ➤ own body
  ➤ luggage

We use these instruments to measure weight:

kitchen scale   bathroom scale   luggage scale   postal scale   baby scale

When measuring weight, you look at:

the number the scale goes up   the unit

Some scales are digital.

Some scales are analogue, just like clocks.

This bag of potatoes weighs 3 kilograms.

We use two main units to measure weight: grams (g) and kilograms (kg).

1 **gram** weighs less than 1 **kilogram**. There are one thousand grams in 1 kilogram.   Two paracetamol tablets weigh 1gram.   A bag of sugar usually weighs 1 kilogram

1 ▷ Write the short form of each unit.

kilogram   gram

____   ____

2 ▷ Which unit is heavier: 1 kilogram or 1 gram? _____

3 ▷ Put these units in order, starting with the heaviest.

5 kilograms   5 grams   50 grams   50 kilograms

_____, _____, _____, _____

4 ⟩ Read the measurements in these scales. Don't forget to add the unit.

_____ _____ _____ _____

5 ⟩ Put the weights of these suitcases in order, starting with the lightest.

22.5kg   19.8kg   21.0kg   20.9kg

_____, _____, _____, _____

6 ⟩ Read the measurements in these scales. Don't forget to add the unit.

_____   _____   _____

7 Jeta is posting a package. The maximum weight the boxes can have is 2kg.

1.5kg   1.9kg   2.2kg

Which of the boxes can Jeta post?

_____

8 Circle the correct answer.

a) The weight of a baby is about:
 	
  10g   10kg
	b) The weight of a plate of pasta is about:
	
	  100g 100kg

c) The weight of a feather is about:
 	
  1g   1kg
	d) The weight of a sandwich is about:
	
	  200g 200kg

9 Gary is making a cake. He needs 100g of sugar. He has 65g of sugar. How much more sugar does he need?

_____

10 Kelly is posting a pallet with furniture to another city. The pallet weighs 17.8kg. The furniture weighs 82.5kg. Kelly thinks that the pallet and the furniture weigh less than 100kg altogether. Is Kelly correct?

_____

11 Sara thinks a TV unit weighs 20g. What is wrong with her answer?

_____

12 Charles thinks 10.0kg is the same as 10kg. Is he correct?

_____

13. Paul is sending a letter by post. The maximum weight should be 100g. He is sending 3 cards, which weigh 30g each. The weight of the envelope is 7g. Can Paul send the letter?

_____

14. Tracey thinks this scale shows 65kg. Is Tracey correct? Why?

_____

_____

Progress check

1. Fill in the gaps below.

The short form of writing **gram** is _____. The short form of writing _____ is **kg**.

2. The weight of a shopping bag is shown in the scales below.

What is the weight of the shopping bag? _____

3. Put these measurements in order, from the smallest to the largest: 1kg , 1g, 50g, 50kg

_____, _____, _____, _____

4. Aaron thinks that 200g is greater than 1kg because 200 is greater than 1. Is he right? Explain your answer.

_____

5. A delivery company charges based on the weight of a package. Here are the charges:

Weight (kg)	Cost
Up to 1 kg	£3
1 - 5 kg	£6
Over 5 kg	£10

Sarah wants to send a package that weighs 4.3 kg. How much will it cost her to send the package?

_____

6. Olivia has three boxes: **Box A** weighs 3.5 kg, **Box B** weighs 1.7 kg, and **Box C** weighs 2.9 kg. What is the total weight of all three boxes in kilograms? You can use a calculator.

_____

Use metric measures of capacity including millilitres and litres

We measure the capacity of items when:

- ➢ cooking
- ➢ storing liquid
- ➢ using bottles
- ➢ getting petrol or diesel
- ➢ administering medicine
- ➢ gardening
- ➢ painting walls

We use these instruments to measure capacity.

| measuring jug | measuring spoons | cylinder | syringe |

To measure capacity:

the unit

the number
the scale goes up
to

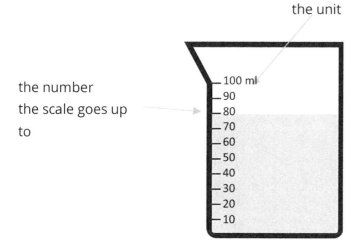

This jug holds 80ml of liquid.

We use two main units to measure
weight: milliliters (ml) and litres (l)

1 **millilitre** weighs less than 1 **litre**.

Medicine is measured in millimetres.

A bottle of oil usually holds 1 litre.
A litre is greater than a millilitre.
There are one thousand millilitres
in a litre.

1. Write the short form of the unit.

     litre   millilitre

     _____   _____

2. Which is greater: 1 litre or 1 millilitre? _____

3. Put these units in order, starting with the highest.

    5 litres   5 millilitres   50 millilitres   50 litres

    _____, _____, _____, _____

4 > How much liquid is there in each container? Include the unit.

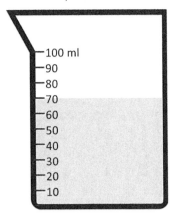 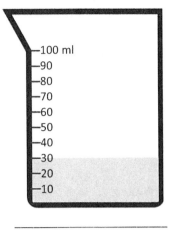 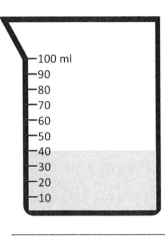

_____ _____ _____

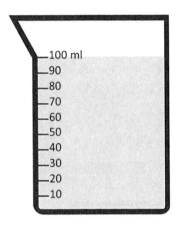 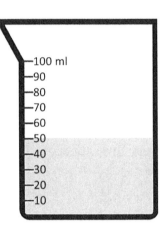

_____ _____ _____

5 > Leni has been given this medicine by the doctor.

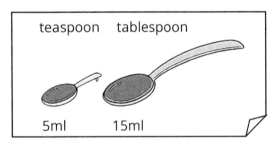

How many teaspoons of medicine should Leni take each day? _____

6 > Kelly needs to fill a bucket with water. The bucket can hold up to 12 liters. She has a jug that holds 1.5 liters. How many full jugs of water will she need to fill the bucket completely? You can use a calculator.

_____

7 > A can of soup contains 0.4 litres of soup. Ann wants to make 1.5 litres of soup.
How many cans of soup does Ann need to buy? Show your working. You can use a calculator.

_____

8 a) Jenny has put this much oil in the measuring jug.

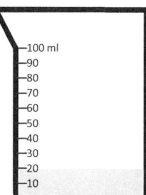

She adds another 70 ml. How much oil is there in total?

_____

b) What fraction of measuring jug has been filled?

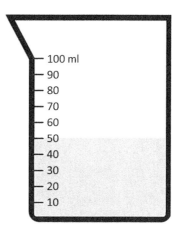

_____

c) One bottle of sunflower oil holds 1 litre.

How many litres of oil are there in 12 bottles?

_____

d) Hoi plans to drink 2 litres of water each day.

How many of these bottles does she drink each day?

_____

e) Bernadette is flying on a plane to go on holiday. She can only take up to 100ml of liquids.

Can they take this sun cream bottle on the plane?

_____

f) This container holds 15 litres of water. Mat is filling 2 litre bottles with the water in this container.

How many full bottles will he be able to fill?

_____

9 Charles thinks 12.0 litres is the same as 12 litres. Is he correct?

_____

10 Circle the correct answer for each question.

a) The capacity of a water bottle is about:

1 millilitre   1 litre

b) The capacity of a bottle is about:

100 millilitres   100 litres

c) The capacity of a water dispenser is about:

10 millilitres   10 litres

11 Put these units in order, starting with the greatest.

7 litres   7 millilitres   70 millilitres   70 litres

_____, _____, _____, _____

12 Gary is making lemonade. He is mixing 70ml lemon juice with 93ml water. How much lemonade is he making?

_____

13 Kelly is filling a paddling pool with buckets of water. The paddling pool needs 96 litres to be filled fully. Each bucket holds 12 litres. Kelly thinks eight buckets are needed to fill the paddling pool.
Is Kelly correct?

_____

14 Sara thinks the rainwater tank in her garden holds 100 millilitres. What is wrong with her answer?

_____

15 A cylinder has 95 ml of liquid in it. If 35 ml is poured out, how much liquid remains in the cylinder? Show your working.

_____

16 Tick the container with the smallest capacity.

A - 75 ml   B - 50 ml   C - 65 ml   D-100ml

1. Fill in the gaps below.

The short form of writing **litre** is _____ . The short form of writing _____ is **ml**.

2. How much liquid is in each container? Include the unit

100 ml	10 litres	100 ml	10 litres
90	9	90	9
80	8	80	8
70	7	70	7
60	6	60	6
50	5	50	5
40	4	40	4
30	3	30	3
20	2	20	2
10	1	10	1

_____   _____   _____   _____

3. Which of the following bottles has a capacity between 40 ml and 60 ml? Tick your answer.

A 35 ml   B 50 ml   C 70 ml

4. A vase can hold 80 ml of water. It is filled with 60 ml of water. How much more water is needed to fill the vase completely? Show your working.

_____

5. A bottle of detergent has a capacity of 98 ml. Half of it is used. How many milliliters of detergent are left in the bottle? Show your working.

_____

6. Sophie has three bottles of vanilla essence. Tick the bottle that has the least amount of vanilla essence.

A 100 ml   B 150 ml   C 125 ml

7. Put these capacities in order, starting with the largest: A 30 ml   B 45 ml   C 25 ml   D 125 ml

_____, _____, _____, _____

8. A recipe calls for 90 ml of milk. There is a measuring cup with 30 ml capacity. How many times should the measuring cup be filled to get the correct amount of milk? Show your working.

_____

9. Tim wants to buy a bottle of soap that holds at least 50 ml. Which bottle should he buy? Tick it.

A 40 ml   B 55 ml   C 45 ml

10. Sam puts 25 ml of water into a 100 ml container. What fraction of the container is filled? _____

Read and compare positive temperatures

We use temperatures when:

> ➤ planning what to wear before going out
> ➤ checking body temperature when unwell
> ➤ planning days out
> ➤ going on holiday
> ➤ cooking
> ➤ heating the house in the winter

To measure temperature, we use these instruments:

weather thermometer   body thermometer

Temperature is usually measured in degrees Celsius (C) or Fahrenheit (F).

In the UK we use Celsius but some countries, like the US, use Fahrenheit.

To measure temperature:

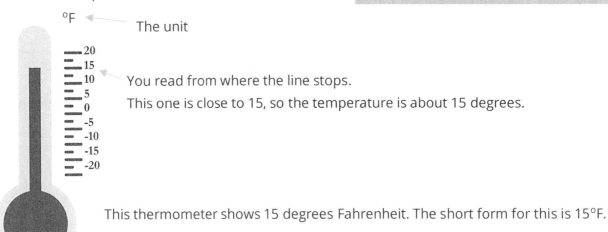

°F ← The unit

You read from where the line stops.
This one is close to 15, so the temperature is about 15 degrees.

This thermometer shows 15 degrees Fahrenheit. The short form for this is 15°F.

The weather temperature can be positive and negative.
Positive temperatures are temperatures higher than 0 degrees. Negative temperatures are temperatures below 0 degrees.

At this level, you only work with positive temperatures.
Important to remember: Water freezes at 0°C. Water boils at 100°C.

1 ▷ Tick the highest temperature.

    16°C   20°C   15°C   24°C

2 ▷ The temperature in Sarah's bedroom is 22°C, while the living room is 18°C. How many degrees warmer is the bedroom compared to the living room?

3 ⟩ Read these temperatures. Include the unit.

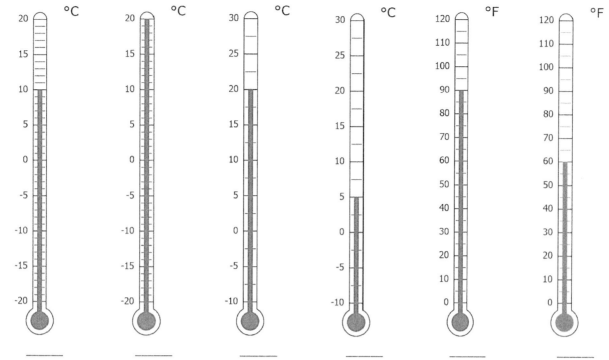

Normal body temperature is between 36 and 37.5 degrees.
Temperatures below 36 and above 37.5 may need medical attention.

4 ⟩ Look at this thermometer.

a) What temperature does this thermometer show? _____ °C
b) Is this a normal body temperature? Why? _____

5 ⟩ a) Which thermometer shows the higher temperature?

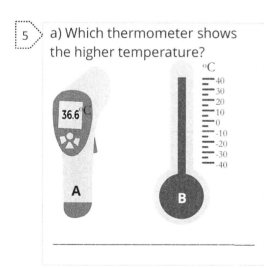

b) Tick the thermometer that shows the highest temperature.

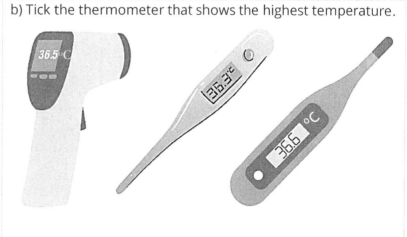

157

6 a) Which thermometer shows the lower temperature?

b) Compare the temperature shown by thermometers A and B.

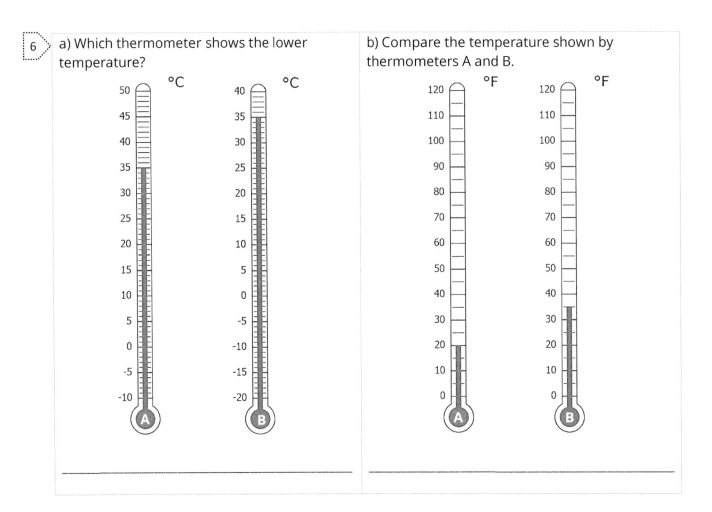

_____

_____

7 Sol thinks this thermometer shows 39°F. Is Sol correct?

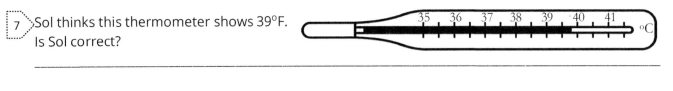

_____

8 a) This is the temperature in the living room. Asha then turns the heating on and the temperature goes up by eight degrees.

What is the new temperature?

_____

b) What is the difference in the temperatures shown in these two thermometers?

_____

_____

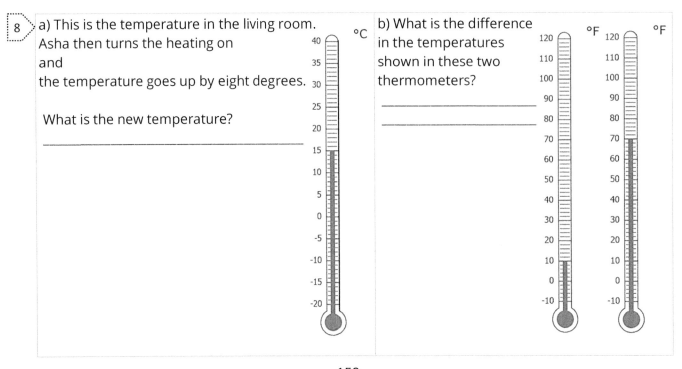

Progress Check

1 Fill in the gaps below.

The short form of writing 20 degree Celsius is _____. Water boils at ___°C. Water _____ at 0°C.

2 Write the temperature shown in the thermometers below.

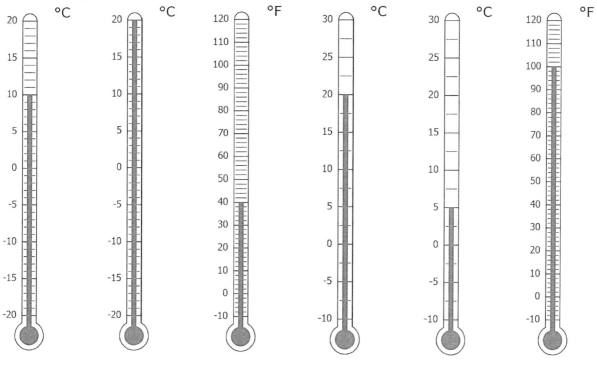

_____ _____ _____ _____ _____ _____

3 a) The fridge temperature should be 4°C or below. Anna's fridge temperature is 6°C. Is Anna's fridge at the right temperature?

_____

b) Anna says: 'The difference between the temperature that the fridge has now and the temperature it should have, is 1°C.' Do you agree?

_____

4 The temperature in offices should be about 18°C. The temperature in an office is 15°C. How many degrees should the temperature increase by to reach 18°C?

_____

5 A room has a temperature of 27°C. Peter wants to cool it down to 20°C using an air conditioner. How many degrees does he need to lower the temperature?

_____

6 The temperature at a bus stop is 2°C. After waiting for 30 minutes, the temperature drops by two degrees. What is the new temperature at the bus stop?

_____

Read and use simple scales to the nearest labelled division

We use the divisions and the numbers when measuring:
- ➢ length
- ➢ weight
- ➢ capacity
- ➢ temperature

Labelled divisions have numbers in them. Unlabelled divisions don't have numbers.

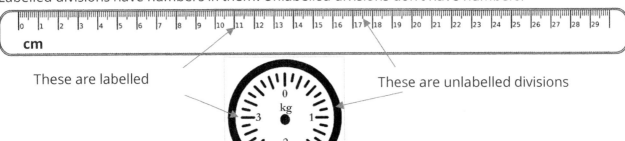

These are labelled

These are unlabelled divisions

At this level, you only do to the nearest **labelled** division.

To the nearest labelled division, this line is 8 cm long.

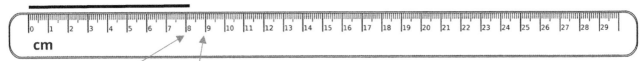

The line is between 8cm and 9cm, but closer to 8cm.

To the nearest labelled division, this line is 22 cm long.

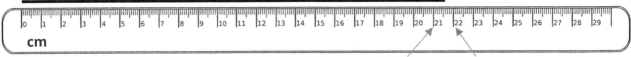

The line is between 21 cm and 22 cm, but closer to 22 cm.

1 ⟩ Read these temperatures to the nearest labelled division.

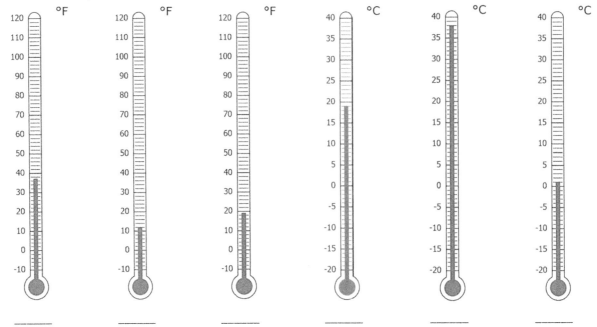

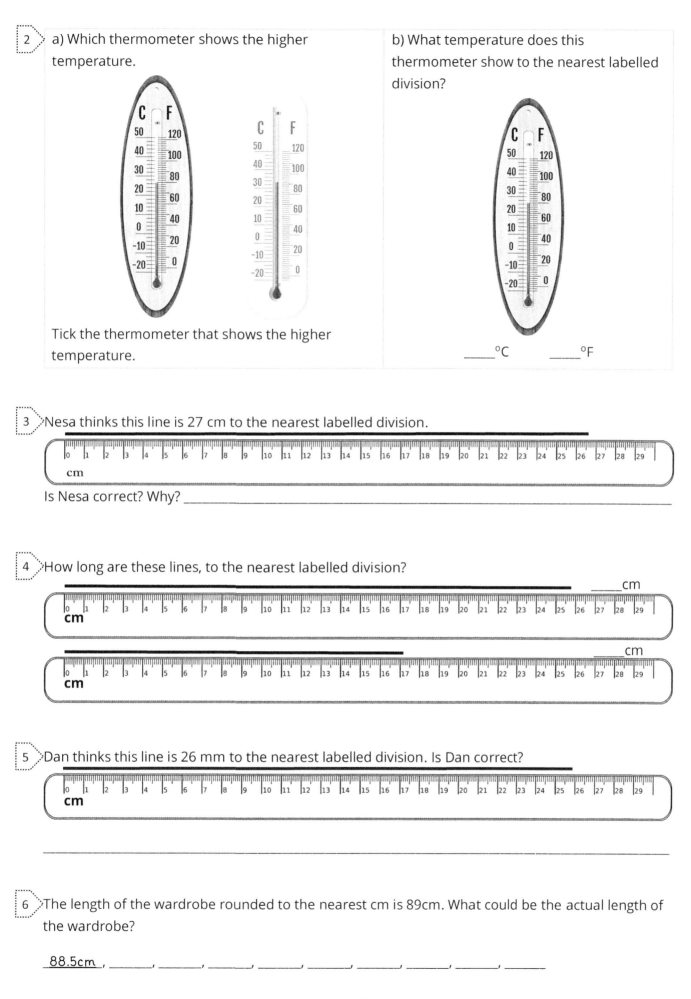

2 a) Which thermometer shows the higher temperature.

Tick the thermometer that shows the higher temperature.

b) What temperature does this thermometer show to the nearest labelled division?

_____ °C   _____ °F

3 Nesa thinks this line is 27 cm to the nearest labelled division.

Is Nesa correct? Why? _____

4 How long are these lines, to the nearest labelled division?

_____ cm

_____ cm

5 Dan thinks this line is 26 mm to the nearest labelled division. Is Dan correct?

_____

6 The length of the wardrobe rounded to the nearest cm is 89cm. What could be the actual length of the wardrobe?

88.5cm , _____, _____, _____, _____, _____, _____, _____, _____, _____

7 ⟩ How much liquid do these measuring jugs hold to the nearest labelled division?

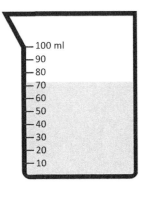 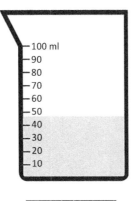 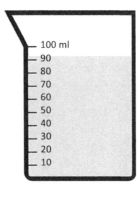 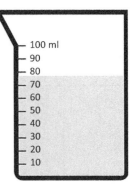

_____ _____ _____ _____

8 ⟩ What are these weights to the nearest labelled division.

_____ _____ _____ _____

9 ⟩
a) What weight does this scale show to the nearest labelled division?

_____

b) Jay thinks this measuring jug holds 1 litre of liquid to the nearest labelled division. Is Jay correct?

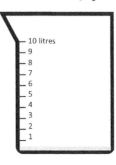

_____

Progress check

1 a) Roughly, how much more liquid is there in cylinder A than B? Include the unit.

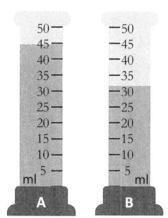

_____

b.i) What is the length of the pencil to the nearest labelled unit? _____

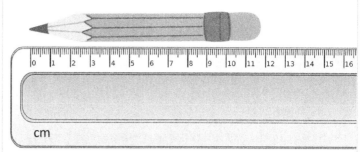

b.ii) Darren has a pencil case which is 10 cm long. Would the pencil above fit in it? Explain your answer.

_____

c) How much does this parcel weigh to the nearest labelled division? Include the unit.

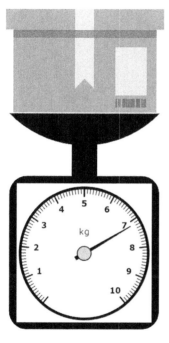

_____

d) Read the temperature shown by each thermometer to the nearest labelled division. Include the unit.

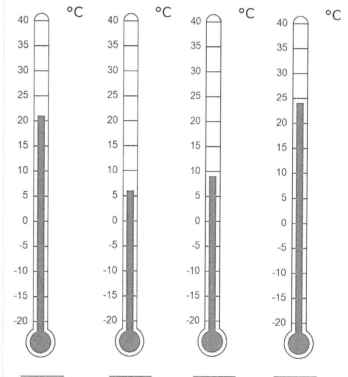

_____   _____   _____   _____

e) Sam wants to frame a picture. She measures the width of the picture, so that she can work out how wide to buy the frame. She adds 1.5cm to each side.

How wide will the frame be?

_____

Recognise and name common 2D and 3D shapes including pentagons, hexagons, cylinders, cuboids, pyramids and spheres

We see shapes around us in:
- ➤ furniture
- ➤ street signs
- ➤ rugs
- ➤ buildings
- ➤ devices
- ➤ jewellery

Identify and recognise common 2D shapes

Shapes can be 2D and 3D.
2D shapes are flat. These are the 2D shapes you need to know at this level.

| square | rectangle | circle | triangle | pentagon | hexagon |

Here are some tricks to remember the names of these 2D shapes.

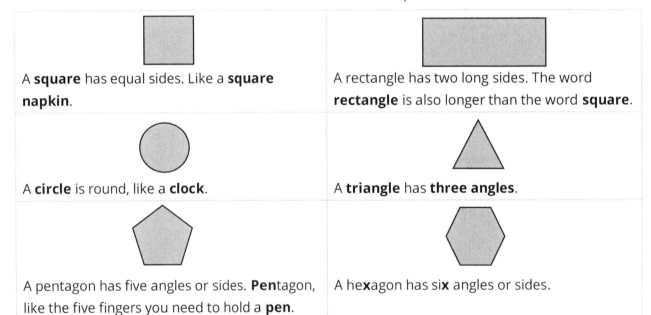

A **square** has equal sides. Like a **square napkin**.	A rectangle has two long sides. The word **rectangle** is also longer than the word **square**.
A **circle** is round, like a **clock**.	A **triangle** has **three angles**.
A pentagon has five angles or sides. **Pen**tagon, like the five fingers you need to hold a **pen**.	A he**x**agon has si**x** angles or sides.

1 ⟩ Match the shapes with the names.

| square | rectangle | circle | triangle | pentagon | hexagon |

2 ⟩ What is the name of the shape that has six sides? _____

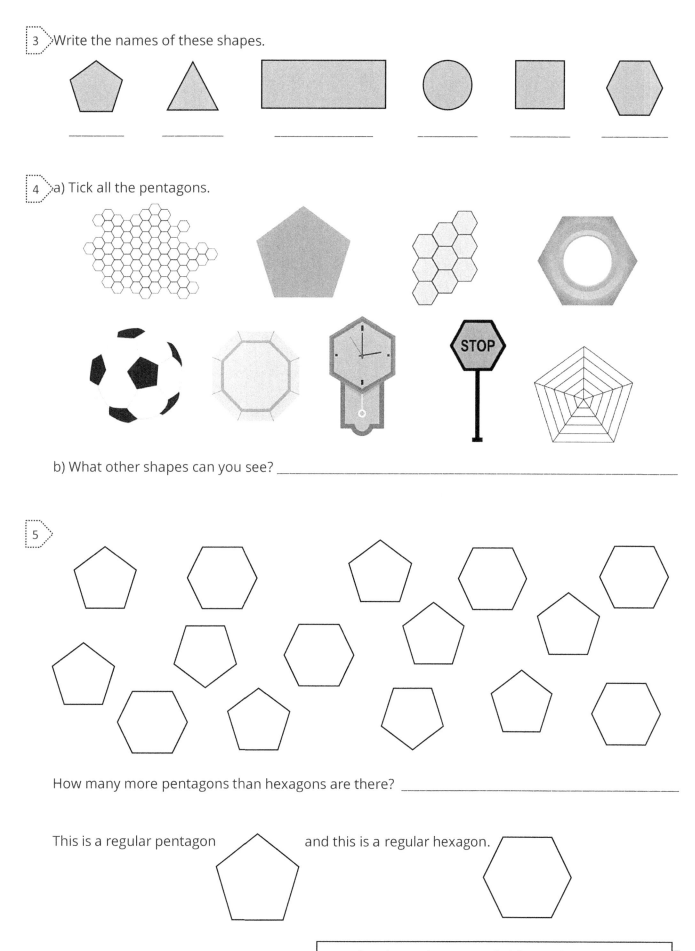

3 Write the names of these shapes.

_____ _____   _____   _____   _____   _____

4 a) Tick all the pentagons.

b) What other shapes can you see? _____

5

How many more pentagons than hexagons are there? _____

This is a regular pentagon   and this is a regular hexagon.

Regular shapes have **equal sides and equal angles.**

165

These are pentagons too, because they have five sides, but they are irregular pentagons.

These are hexagons too, because they have six sides, but they are irregular hexagons.

6 ⟩ Draw these shapes. The hexagon and the pentagon can be irregular.

pentagon   rectangle   hexagon   triangle

7 ⟩ Write these words again and again.

square, _____, _____, _____, _____, _____, _____, _____, _____

rectangle, _____, _____, _____, _____, _____, _____, _____, _____

circle, _____, _____, _____, _____, _____, _____, _____, _____

triangle, _____, _____, _____, _____, _____, _____, _____, _____

pentagon, _____, _____, _____, _____, _____, _____, _____, _____

hexagon, _____, _____, _____, _____, _____, _____, _____, _____

8 ⟩ Zoi's rug is in the shape of a hexagon. Tick the hexagon.

9 ⟩ What is the name of the shape that has five sides? _____

10 ⟩ Tick the shape that has the highest number of sides?

Identify and recognize common 3D shapes

3D shapes are not flat. These are the 3D shapes you need to know at this level.

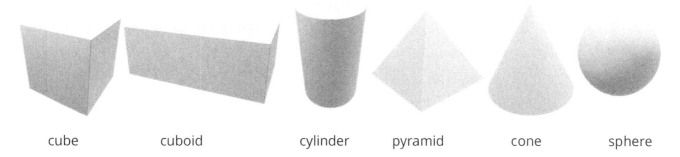

| cube | cuboid | cylinder | pyramid | cone | sphere |

Here are some tricks to remember the names of these 3D shapes.

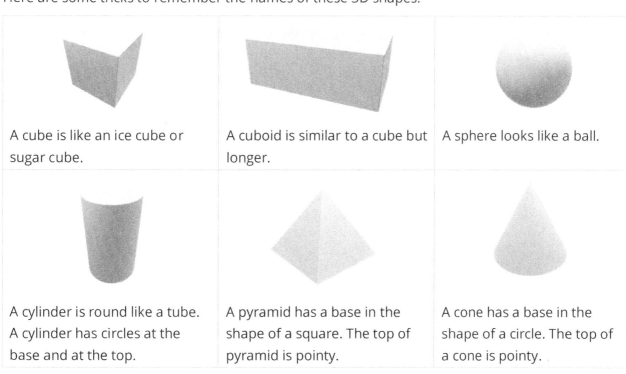

A cube is like an ice cube or sugar cube.

A cuboid is similar to a cube but longer.

A sphere looks like a ball.

A cylinder is round like a tube. A cylinder has circles at the base and at the top.

A pyramid has a base in the shape of a square. The top of pyramid is pointy.

A cone has a base in the shape of a circle. The top of a cone is pointy.

11 Fill the gaps.

| c_ne | sp_ere | c_be | cub_id | pyram_d | c_linder |

12 Match each shape with its name.

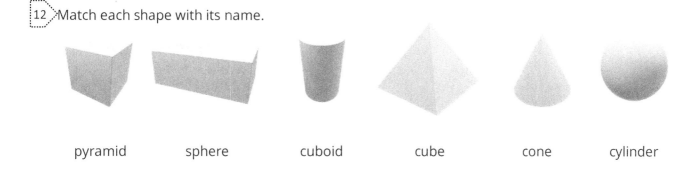

| pyramid | sphere | cuboid | cube | cone | cylinder |

13 Name these shapes.

14 Write these words again and again.

cube _____, _____, _____, _____, _____, _____

cuboid _____, _____, _____, _____, _____

cone _____, _____, _____, _____, _____

pyramid _____, _____, _____, _____, _____

cylinder _____, _____, _____, _____, _____

sphere _____, _____, _____, _____, _____

15 Add the names of all the shapes you know, under the correct heading.

2D Shape	3D Shapes
square	cuboid

16 Write the names of these shapes.

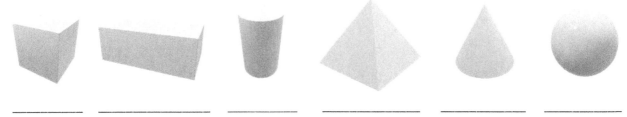

_____ _____ _____ _____ _____ _____

Progress check

1 Draw each of the shapes named below:

Triangle	Square	Pentagon	Circle	Rectangle	Hexagon

2 Look at these shapes. How many more 2D than 3D shapes are there? _____

3 Andy thinks that the rug below is in the shape of a square. Is he right? Why?

_____

_____

4 Magda calls this shape 'sphere'. Is she correct? Why?

_____

_____

5 Zuri has bought this storage box for clothes.

What shape is the storage box in? _____

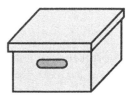

Describe the properties of common 2D and 3D shapes including number of sides, corners, edges, faces, angles and base

We think of properties of shapes when:

> ➢ ordering furniture
> ➢ storing food
> ➢ storing boxes
> ➢ organising cupboards
> ➢ putting items next to each other

2D shapes have sides and angles. These are the **sides** of a rectangle.

These are the **angles** of a rectangle.

Properties of 2D shapes.

4 sides 4 angles	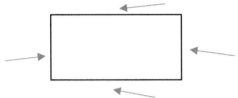	4 sides 4 angles		3 sides 3 angles	
0 sides 0 angles		5 sides 5 angles		6 sides 6 angles	

1 a) Write the names of all of the 2D shapes you know that have 4 sides.

_____

b) Write the names of all of the 2D shapes you know that have 3 angles.

_____

c) Which 2D shape has no sides and no angles?

_____

2 Alice is buying a new dining table. She will put it in a corner of the kitchen. The tables she likes look like this from the top.

Tick the shapes that are more suitable to put in the corner of the kitchen.

3 John has printed a picture on an A4 piece of paper. He wants to frame it. What shape should he buy the frame in?

_____

These are the faces, the edges and the base of a 3D shape.

The faces of a pyramid are the 2D shapes you see when rotating the shape. This pyramid has 5 faces

The base is what the shape sits on. This pyramid has a square base.

The edges are the lines where the faces meet. This pyramid has 8 edges.

Properties of 3D shapes.

| 6 faces 12 edges square base | | 3 faces 2 edges circle base | | 6 faces 12 edges rectangle or square base | |
| 2 faces 1 edge circle base | | 1 face 0 edges no base | | 5 faces 8 edges square base | |

4 a) Which 3D shapes have 6 faces? _____

   b) Which 3D shape has no edges and no base? _____

   c) Which 3D shapes have 12 edges? _____

   d) Which 3D shape 3 faces and 2 edges? _____

   e) How many faces does a cuboid have? _____

   f) How many faces does a cylinder have? _____

   g) How many edges does a cube have? _____

   h) What shape does the base of a cylinder have? _____

   i) How many edges does a square-based pyramid have? _____

5 John is building a shed in the garden. The roof of the shed will be in the shape of square-based pyramid. What shape will the floor of the shed be in? _____

6 a) Lorna has bought a new cabinet for the hallway. What shape is the base of the cabinet in?

   _____

   b) Should the cabinet fit into a corner of the hallway?

   _____

A right angle is the angle you see in corners of rooms or corners of sheets of paper.

A square has 4 right angles. A rectangle has 4 right angles.

Regular pentagons or hexagons have no right angles.

7 > Tick the shapes with right angles.

Progress check

1 > Write how many sides, corners and right angles each of the shapes below has.

___ sides ___ angles	___ sides ___ angles	___ sides ___ angles
___ sides ___ angles	___ sides ___ angles	___ sides ___ angles

2 > Which of the shapes above have 4 sides? _____

3 > Tick the shapes below that have more than one right angle?

4 > Write how many edges and faces each of the shapes below has. Also, write what shape is the base.

___ faces ___ edges _____ base	___ faces ___ edges _____ base	6 faces 12 edges _____ base
___ faces ___ edge _____ base	___ face ___ edges _____ base	___ faces ___ edges _____ base

5 > Andy says that the base of a cube is always square. Is this true? _____

6 > Magda thinks that a square-based pyramid has 5 edges. Is she right? Why?

_____

Use appropriate positional vocabulary to describe position and direction including between, inside, outside, middle, below, on top, forwards and backwards

We use positional vocabulary to:
- ➤ describe the position of a building
- ➤ give directions to a place or item
- ➤ follow instructions
- ➤ give instructions
- ➤ locate items around the house

These are some examples of how the words **between**, **inside**, **outside**, **middle**, **below**, **on top**, **forwards** and **backwards** can be used.

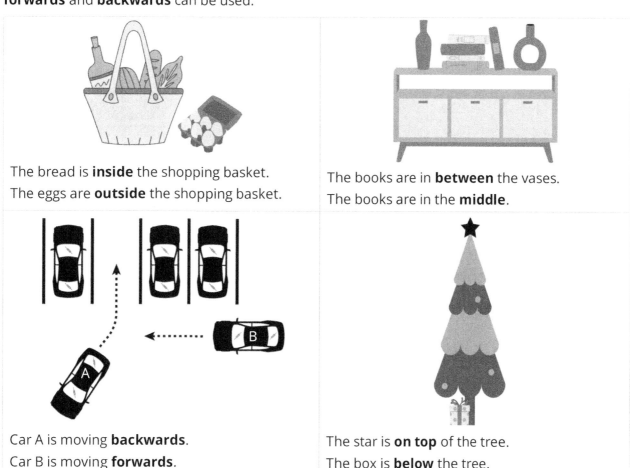

The bread is **inside** the shopping basket.
The eggs are **outside** the shopping basket.

The books are in **between** the vases.
The books are in the **middle**.

Car A is moving **backwards**.
Car B is moving **forwards**.

The star is **on top** of the tree.
The box is **below** the tree.

1 ▷ Fill the gaps with the words **on top of** or **below**.

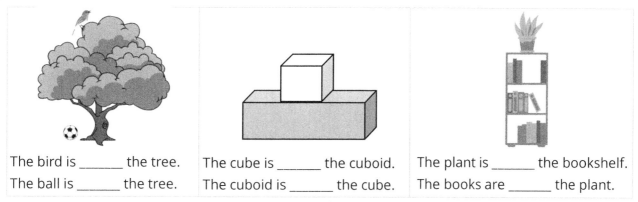

The bird is _____ the tree.
The ball is _____ the tree.

The cube is _____ the cuboid.
The cuboid is _____ the cube.

The plant is _____ the bookshelf.
The books are _____ the plant.

2 Fill the gaps with the words **inside** or **outside**.

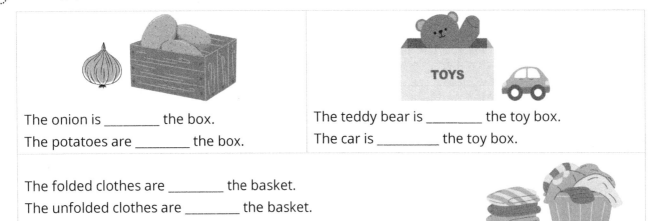

The onion is _____ the box.
The potatoes are _____ the box.

The teddy bear is _____ the toy box.
The car is _____ the toy box.

The folded clothes are _____ the basket.
The unfolded clothes are _____ the basket.

3 Fill the gaps with the words **forwards** or **backwards**.

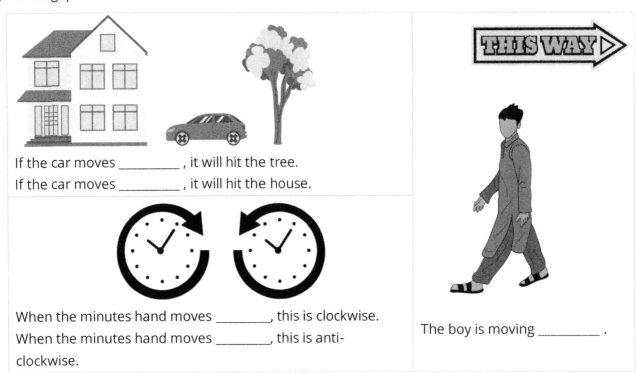

If the car moves _____ , it will hit the tree.
If the car moves _____ , it will hit the house.

When the minutes hand moves _____, this is clockwise.
When the minutes hand moves _____, this is anti-clockwise.

The boy is moving _____ .

4 Fill the gaps with the words **top**, **between** and **middle**.

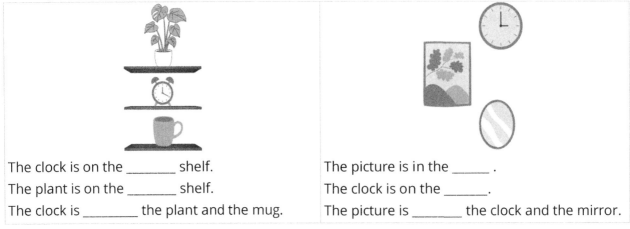

The clock is on the _____ shelf.
The plant is on the _____ shelf.
The clock is _____ the plant and the mug.

The picture is in the _____ .
The clock is on the _____.
The picture is _____ the clock and the mirror.

174

5 Fill the gaps.

a)

The bag is on top of
_____ .
The computer is below
_____ .
The computer is _____ the lamp and the pens.
_____ is in the middle.

b)

The bathroom is inside
_____.
_____ is outside the house.
The loft is on the _____ floor.

c)

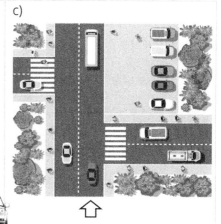

You are in this car. Your friend is with you.
Your friend says: "To get to the car park, you need to move backwards and then turn right". Is your friend correct? Why?
_____

Progress check

1 Complete the sentences below with the words **between**, **in the middle**, **below** or **on top of**.

The sphere is _____ the cylinder.
The cylinder is _____ cube and the cuboid.
The cube is _____ the cylinder.
The shape _____ is called a cylinder.

2 a) Complete the sentences below using: **inside** or **outside**.

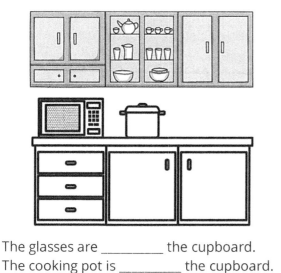

The glasses are _____ the cupboard.
The cooking pot is _____ the cupboard.

b) Complete the sentences below using: **forwards** or **backwards**.

If the bike moves _____, it will hit the tree.
If the bike moves _____, it will hit the lamppost.

Extract information from lists, tables, diagrams and bar charts

We extract information from:

> ➢ menus
> ➢ receipts
> ➢ timetables
> ➢ maps

Extract information from lists

Greta is buying a pizza from the local pizza shop.

How much does the Margherita Pizza cost?

Pizza Place

Margherita Pizza	£12
Vegetable Pizza	£11
Pepperoni Pizza	£14

Which pizza costs £11?

---

1) Nala went shopping at the weekend. This is the receipt she got.

a) How much did the shoes cost? _____

b) What cost more: the coat or the shoes? _____

c) Which is the cheapest item in the receipt? _____

d) Which items cost £8? _____

e) How much did all the items cost? Use a calculator to work out the total. _____

CASH RECEIPT

Description	Price
T-shirt	£17.00
Coat	£36.00
Shoes	£42.00
Belt	£8.00
Total	

#8549265935593559346#

---

2) a) The list below shows the schedule of activities at a summer camp.

Summer Camp Activities:

Monday: Arts and Crafts
Tuesday: Swimming
Wednesday: Hiking
Thursday: Swimming
Friday: Nature Walk

i) On which two days do the campers go swimming?

_____

ii) On which day do the campers go hiking?

_____

iii) What do the campers do on Friday?

_____

b) Peter goes to a bakery to buy some pastries.

Menu:

Chocolate Chip Cookie
Blueberry Muffin
Plain Croissant
Chocolate Éclair
Raspberry Tart

i) Which two pastries have chocolate in them?

_____

ii) How many items are there on the menu?

_____

iii) Which item is the last on the menu?

_____

Progress check

1. Sal is ordering some items from an online shop.

    a) How much does the utensil set cost? _____

    b) How much does the wooden spoon cost? _____

    c) Which item is the most expensive? _____

    d) How much does the first item in the list cost? _____

    e) The pack of batteries costs £4. How much does one battery cost? _____

    f) Use a calculator to work out the total cost. _____

Your basket

Batteries (pack of 4)	£4
Alarm clock	£12
Utensil set	£10
Wooden spoon	£5

2. Tim visits a café and is looking at the menu.

Menu

Chicken Burger	£3
Grilled Cheese Sandwich (Vegetarian)	£3
Spaghetti Bolognese	£5
Fish and Chips	£4
Vegetable Curry (Vegetarian)	£5

a) How much does spaghetti Bolognese cost? _____

b) How much more than a chicken burger does a vegetable curry cost?

_____

c) If you paid for a grilled cheese sandwich with a £10 note, how much change would you be given?

_____

d) Tim wants to buy the cheapest vegetarian food available. How much does it cost?_____

3. This timetable shows the times planes are leaving and the gate numbers.

a) What time is the Aberdeen flight taking off?

_____

b) From which gate is the Cape Town flight taking off?

_____

c) Which flight takes off at 17:00?

_____

d) Which flight will take off after the Dubai one?

_____

12:00	New York	Gate 83
15:00	Aberdeen	Gate 31
17:00	Glasgow	Gate 97
18:00	Cape Town	Gate 94
19:00	Dubai	Gate 15
20:00	Nice	Gate 52

Extract information from tables

Maria wants to buy a shirt from an online store. The available shirt colors and their prices are listed below. Maria wants a blue shirt.

How much does the <u>blue shirt</u> cost?

Colour	Price
Red	£12
Blue	£15
Green	£10

Which shirt costs <u>£10</u>?

1) A college offers these courses.

a) What day does the maths course run on? _____

b) What day does the English course run on? _____

c) Which course is the last in the table? _____

d) Which course is the third in the table? _____

e) Which course runs on Thursday? _____

f) Which course runs on Friday? _____

Course	Day	Time
English	Tuesday	9-11am
Maths	Monday	12-2pm
IT	Friday	6-8pm
Biology	Wednesday	9-11am
Chemistry	Thursday	12-2pm
Physics	Saturday	9-11am

g) What time does the physics course run on? _____

h) What time does the biology course run on? _____

i) What time does the Friday course run on? _____

2) Nora is looking at the weather forecast for next week.

Monday	Tuesday	Wednesday	Thursday	Friday	Saturday	Sunday
18°C	19°C	16°C	22°C	18°C	21°C	20°C

a) What's the temperature on Sunday? _____

b) On which day is the temperature 16°C? _____

c) On which day is the temperature the highest? _____

3) The table below shows the distance covered by different coaches from the coach station to different cities.

a) Which destination is 68 miles away from the bus station?

_____

b) Which destination is 38 miles away from the bus station?

_____

Destination	Distance (miles)
City A	55
City B	42
City C	68
City D	38

c) How many miles from the bus station is City A?

_____

d) How many miles further is City A than City D?

_____

Progress check

1. Information about Prevent referral cases is represented in this table.

a) How many 31to 40-year-olds were referred?

_____

b) Which of the groups had most of the referrals?

_____

c) How many more 21-30 than 31–40-year-olds were referred?

_____

d) There were 10 referrals for the age group 41 and over. Add this information to the table.

e) Work out the total number of referrals.

_____

Prevent referrals by age in winter 2021-2022	
Age	**Number of case (to the nearest 10)**
Under 15	60
15-20	60
21-30	20
31-40	10
41 and over	___

2. The table below displays the opening hours of a library.

a) What time does the library close on Tuesday?

_____

b) On which day is the library closed?

_____

Day	**Opening hours**
Monday	09:00 – 17:00
Tuesday	09:00 – 17:00
Wednesday	Closed
Thursday	09:00 – 17:00
Friday	09:00 – 17:00

3. The table below shows the number of Pages in four different books.

a) Which book has the lowest number of Pages?

_____

b) How many Pages does Book B have?

_____

c) What is the difference in the number of Pages for books A and D?

_____

Book	**Pages**
Book A	120
Book B	195
Book C	175
Book D	200

4. Jack looks at this weather forecast table.

a) What is the weather forecast for Wednesday?

_____

b) Which day will be rainy?

_____

c) How many days will be sunny?

_____

Day	**Weather**
Monday	Sunny
Tuesday	Rainy
Wednesday	Cloudy
Thursday	Sunny

d) On Friday the weather will be rainy. Add this to the table.

Extract information from diagrams

This diagram is a family tree.

Malik and Emily have two children: Harper and Brandon.

Brandon is married to Ava. They have two children: Samuel and Isabella.

1 This is a diagram of a business building.

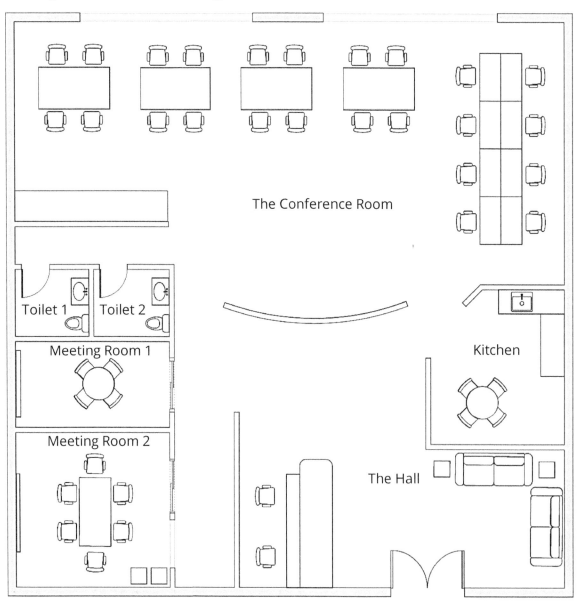

a) How many chairs are there in the conference room? _____

b) How many meeting rooms are there? _____

c) The kitchen is in between _____ and _____ .

Progress check

1) This is a diagram of some train routes.

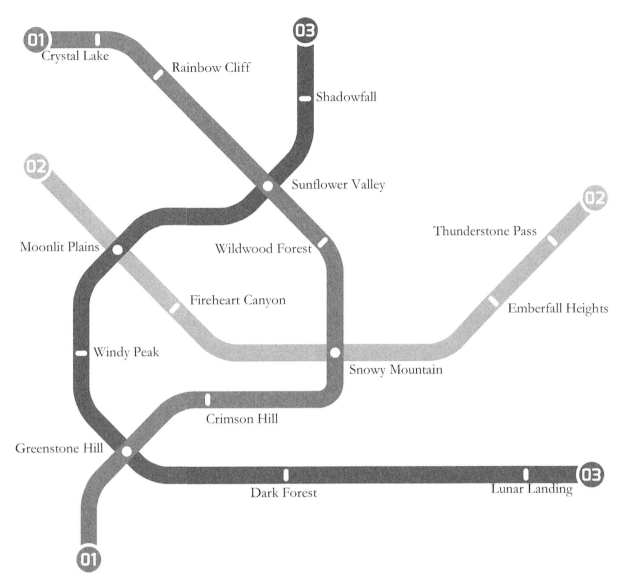

a) Which route is Crimson Hill in? Circle the correct option: Route 01   Route 02   Route 03

b) Isla is travelling from Greenstone Hill to Sunflower Valley. How many stops are there in between?

_____

c) Write the names of the stops between Moonlit Plains and Thunderstone Pass.

_____

2) This is a food diet that Heather follows.

a) What fraction of the whole diet is made of grains? _____

b) Which of the sources of food has the highest portion?

_____

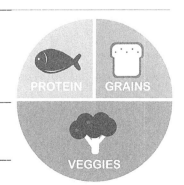

Extract information from bar charts

1 ⟩ This is the number of students in each maths class at MarsCademy College.

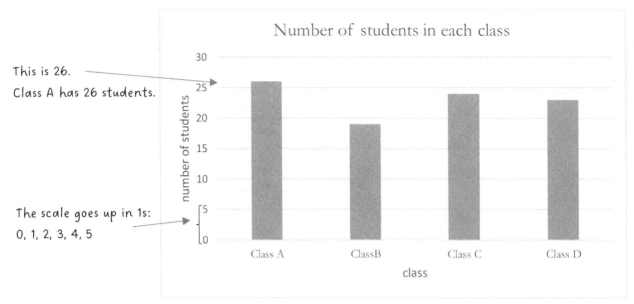

This is 26.
Class A has 26 students.

The scale goes up in 1s:
0, 1, 2, 3, 4, 5

a) How many students are there in Class B? _____

b) How many students are there in class D? _____

c) Which class has the highest number of students? _____

2 ⟩ This is how much Sunny spent on food last month.

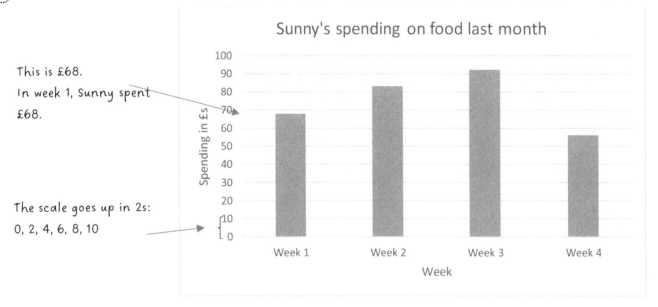

This is £68.
In week 1, Sunny spent £68.

The scale goes up in 2s:
0, 2, 4, 6, 8, 10

a) How much did Sunny spend in week 3? _____

b) How much did Sunny spend in week 4? _____

c) In which week did he spend the lowest amount? _____

Progress check

1 Samina recorded how many minutes she exercised for each day last week.

a) How many minutes did she exercise for on Monday? _____

b) Samina exercised for 5 minutes on Friday. Add this to the bar chart.

c) Which day did Samina exercise the most? _____

d) On which day did Samina exercise for 30 minutes? _____

e) On which days did Samina have a break from exercising? _____

2 Nita works as a delivery driver. This is how far she travelled each day last week.

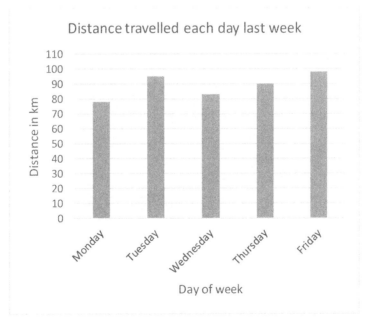

a) On which days did Nita travel more than 90km? _____

b) On which day did she travel the least? _____

c) On which day did she travel 98km? _____

Make numerical comparisons from bar charts

1. Shobna has her own business. This is how many items she sold from January to April last year.

a) How many more items did she sell in January than in February? _____

b) In which months did she sell less than 50 items? _____

c) In which month did she sell the least number of items? _____

2. This bar chart shows how many books Gary read each year from 2020 to 2022.

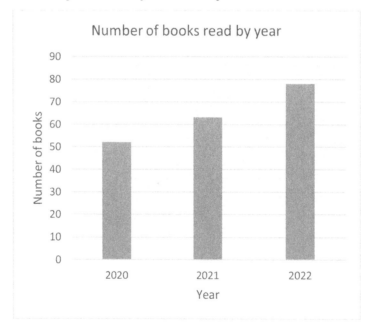

a) In which year did Gary read the highest number of books? _____

b) How many more books did Gary read in 2022 than in 2020? _____

c) In which years did Gary read more than 60 books? _____

d) Describe the reading trend for Gary, from 2020 to 2022.

_____

3) This is how much rubbish was recycled in a recycling centre last year.

a) Which material is the most recycled one? _____

b) How many more tons of paper than glass were recycled? _____

c) Which material has less than 30 tons of recycling material? _____

d) Which material is the least recycled one? _____

4) Colleagues at work are voting on whether they should work from home. These are the results.

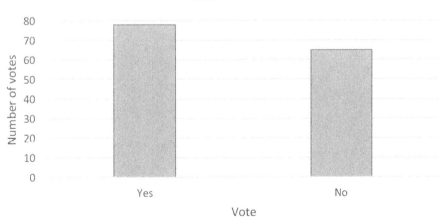

a) How many colleagues prefer to work from home? _____

b) Which option has most of the votes? _____

c) How many more prefer to work from home than not? _____

d) Zerina thinks only half of the number who voted YES, voted NO. Is she correct?

_____

1 Here is some information about sales of a small business during April, May, June and July in 2022.

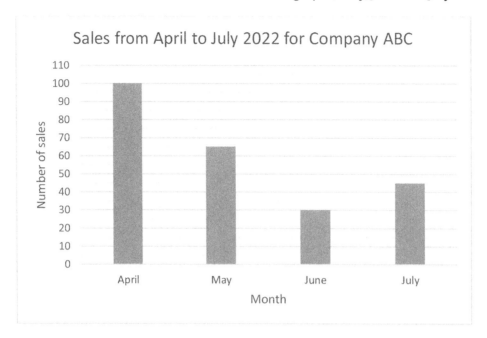

a) In which months did Company ABC make more than 50 sales?

_____

b) In which month did Company ABC have the highest number of sales?

_____

2 This is the number of students in each maths class at MarsCademy College.

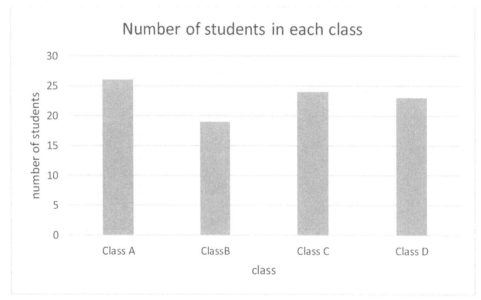

a) Which classes have fewer than 25 students?

_____

b) Which classes have between 20 and 25 students?

_____

Sort and classify objects using two criteria

We sort clothes and classify:

> ➢ clothes
> ➢ rubbish
> ➢ shapes
> ➢ food
> ➢ money
> ➢ documents

These clothes have been sorted into tops/trousers. This is the first criterion.

Then the clothes have been sorted into short-sleeved and long-sleeved. This is the second criteron.

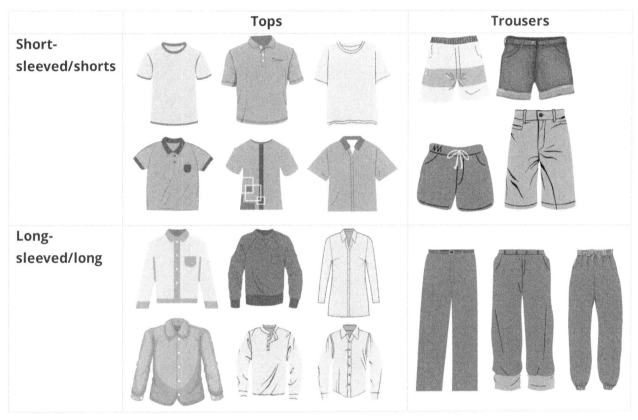

	Tops	Trousers
Short-sleeved/shorts		
Long-sleeved/long		

Another example of sorting clothes is into washed/unwashed and dark/light colours.

> We say one **criterion** and two **criteria**.

1. Tick the small white triangles.

2. Nas works in a shop. He is sorting the items into coats and dresses. He then sorts the items by price. Match the items with the rail they should go to.

3 > Gary ticked some of these shapes, following two criteria.

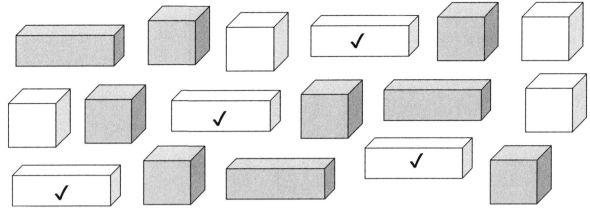

What was the criteria he used?

_____

4 > Circle all the numbers that are odd and smaller than 20.

8   15   100   19   18   21   10   72   91

5 > Fiona has these coins and notes in her purse.

  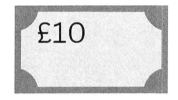

How many coins and notes with a value greater than £1 does Fiona have in her purse? _____

6 > Add the headings.

Progress check

1 ▷ Lorna found clothes she likes in a shop. She wants to buy a top that costs less than £10. Tick the clothes that meet these criteria.

2 ▷ Sunjeong was given these shapes to sort. She ticked two of the shapes below.

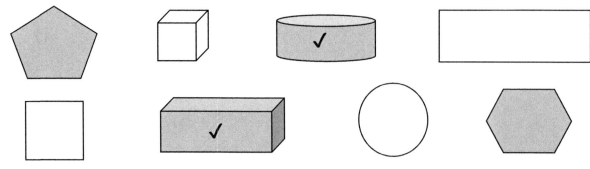

What criteria was she given? _____

3 ▷ Alan was asked to find an odd number greater than 15 and his answer was 16. Is he right? Explain why.

_____

Take info from one format and represent the information in another format including the use of bar charts

We use simple charts and diagrams to help us make decisions.

Wadhah asked the students in Class K about the subjects they want to study next year, out of construction, hairdressing and business. He collected the responses in a tally chart.
Wadhah is showing the information collected to his colleagues in a bar chart.

The title explains what the bar chart is about.

Subject	Tally
construction	|||| ||||	
hairdressing	|||| ||||
business	|||| |||| |||

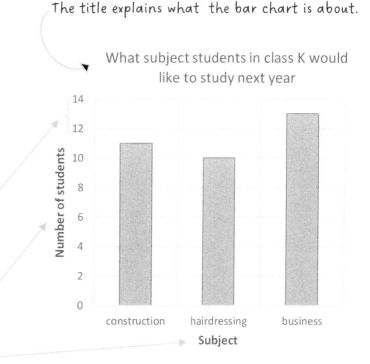

The scale goes up in twos, to 14. Business has the highest (13 students) and 14 covers that.

The axes have been labelled to tell the reader what the numbers and construction, hairdressing and business mean.

1 > Jackie is a teacher at MarsCademy College. She is teaching a lesson on the environment and the carbon footprint. She collected information about how students in MarsCademy College travel to college.

Mode of travel	Number of students
walk	20
bus	13
train	15
bike	18

How students travel to MarsCademy College

Show the missing information in the bar chart.

2 > Oli works in a bedroom furniture shop. He is checking the stock levels for different items.

beds	18
wardrobes	15
bedside tables	19
dressing tables	12
mirrors	17

Show this information in a bar chart.

3 > Sammy is showing her staff the number of items they have sold each month for the last six months. Show this information in the table.

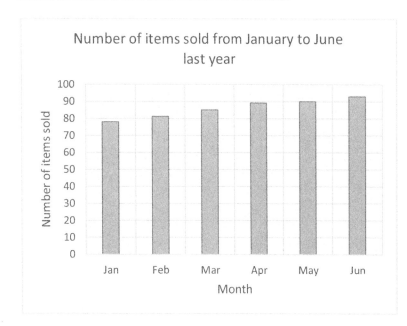

Month	Number of items sold

3 > Find three mistakes with this bar chart.

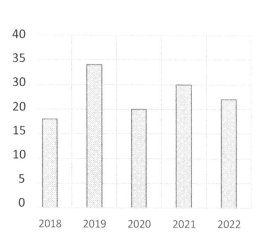

1. _____

2. _____

3. _____

1. Information about Prevent referral cases has been represented in a table and bar chart below. Complete the table and the bar chart.

Prevent referrals by age in winter 2021-2022	
Age (in years)	**Number of cases (rounded to the nearest 10)**
Under 15	60
15-20	___
21-30	20
31-40	10
41 and over	___

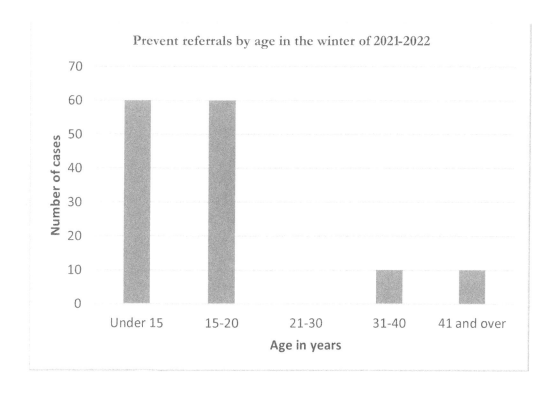

Prevent referrals by age in the winter of 2021-2022

Practice Paper

Part A (Non-calculator) **25 minutes** **7 marks in total**

1 Write the number **81** in words.

_____(1 mark)

2 There are 43 students enrolled on a maths course at college. 86 students are enrolled on an English course. How many students are enrolled on the English and maths courses?

_____(2 marks)

3 Zoe is buying a pair of shoes for £36. She pays with a £50 note. Zoe thinks she will get £24 change. Is she correct? Show your working.

_____(2 marks)

4 Lena is going to the library at the time shown by the clock. She thinks this is quarter past twelve.

Is she correct? Why?

_____(2 marks)

1 ▷ Suki is counting the number of plants in her house.

How many plants does Suki have in her house?

_____(1 mark)

2 ▷ Elaine is working out 5 **times** 12.

| 5 – 12 = | 5 + 12 = | 5 x 12 = | 12 ÷ 5 = |

Tick the option that shows how Elaine can work this out.

(1 mark)

3 ▷ Write these numbers in order, starting with the smallest: **120   81   55   101**

_____, _____, _____, _____

(1 mark)

4 ▷ Darren is cooking for a charity event. He needs 20 eggs.

Eggs in the shop come in cartons of 6 only.

How many cartons of eggs should he buy?

_____(2 marks)

5 ▷ What is the name of this shape?

_____

(1 mark)

6 ▷ The door numbers on a street go like this: 63, 65, 67, ___, ___

Write the door numbers of the next two houses on the street.

(2 marks)

7 ▷ Jo is sixty-nine years old. Write **sixty-eight** in digits.

_____(1 mark)

8 > Wendy is paying for a train ticket. The train ticket is £27.

ONE POUND TWO POUNDS ONE POUND TWO POUNDS ONE POUND TWO POUNDS ONE POUND

£5   £10   £5

Tick the coins and notes Wendy can use to pay for the train ticket.   (2 marks)

9 > a) Tick all the small footballs.

b) How many more small basketballs than big footballs are there?

_____(2 marks)

10 > Magda is posting four items. This is how much they weigh.

2.0 kg   1.5 kg   1.0 kg   1.1 kg

She sends the item that weighs the most first. Tick the item that Magda will send first.   (1 mark)

11 > Helen is buying a new dining table. The dining table costs £100. Helen will pay a quarter of the cost on the first day and the rest of the amount later.

a) How much will Helen pay on the first day?

_____(2 marks)

b) How much will Helen pay later?

_____(1 mark)

12 > Liz works 48 weeks in a year. How many weeks is Liz not working for?

_____(1 mark)

13 Jo works in a shop. She has been told to put a box on the middle shelf.
Circle the shelf Jo should put the box on.

(1 mark)

14 Gary is making a cake. He needs to put 80ml of oil in the cake.
This is how much oil he has put in the measuring jug.

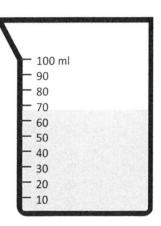

Is this enough? Give a reason for your answer.

_____(1 mark)

15 Sunjeong keeps track of how much exercise she does each day for a week. This is how many minutes she exercised for each day.

Day	Exercise in minutes
Monday	35
Tuesday	44
Wednesday	25
Thursday	23
Friday	32
Saturday	45
Sunday	60

On which days did Sunjeong exercise for less than half an hour?

_____(1 mark)

Answers

Read and write numbers up to 200

Q1. Page 7

1	2	3	4	5	6	7	8	9	10
11	12	13	14	15	16	17	18	19	20
21	22	23	24	25	26	27	28	29	30
31	32	33	34	35	36	37	38	39	40
41	42	43	44	45	46	47	48	49	50
51	52	53	54	55	56	57	58	59	60
61	62	63	64	65	66	67	68	69	70
71	72	73	74	75	76	77	78	79	80
81	82	83	84	85	86	87	88	89	90
91	92	93	94	95	96	97	98	99	100

Q2. Page 7

1	2	**3**	4	**5**	6	**7**	8	**9**	10
11	12	**13**	14	**15**	16	**17**	18	**19**	20
21	22	**23**	24	**25**	26	**27**	28	**29**	30
31	32	**33**	34	**35**	36	**37**	38	**39**	40
41	42	**43**	44	**45**	46	**47**	48	**49**	50
51	52	**53**	54	**55**	56	**57**	58	**59**	60
61	62	**63**	64	**65**	66	**67**	68	**69**	70
71	72	**73**	74	**75**	76	**77**	78	**79**	80
81	82	**83**	84	**85**	86	**87**	88	**89**	90
91	92	**93**	94	**95**	96	**97**	98	**99**	100

Q3. Page 8

1	**2**	3	**4**	5	**6**	7	**8**	9	**10**
11	12	**13**	14	**15**	16	**17**	18	**19**	20
21	**22**	23	**24**	25	**26**	27	**28**	29	**30**
31	32	**33**	34	**35**	36	**37**	38	**39**	40
41	**42**	43	**44**	45	**46**	47	**48**	49	**50**
51	52	**53**	54	**55**	56	**57**	58	**59**	60
61	**62**	63	**64**	65	**66**	67	**68**	69	**70**
71	72	**73**	74	**75**	76	**77**	78	**79**	80
81	**82**	83	**84**	85	**86**	87	**88**	89	**90**
91	92	**93**	94	**95**	96	**97**	98	**99**	100

Q4. Page 8

one, **two**, three, **four**, five, **six**, seven, eight, nine, ten

eleven, twelve, thirteen, fourteen, fifteen, sixteen, seventeen, eighteen, nineteen, twenty

twenty one, twenty two, twenty three, twenty four, twenty five, twenty six, twenty seven, twenty eight, twenty nine, thirty

thirty one, thirty two, thirty three, thirty four, thirty five, thirty six, thirty seven, thirty eight, thirty nine, forty

forty one, forty two, forty three, forty four, forty five, forty six, forty seven, forty eight, forty nine, fifty

fifty one, fifty two, fifty three, fifty four, fifty five, fifty six, fifty seven, fifty eight, fifty nine, sixty

sixty one, sixty two, sixty three, sixty four, sixty five, sixty six, sixty seven, sixty eight, sixty nine, seventy,

seventy one, seventy two, seventy three, seventy four, seventy five, seventy six, seventy seven, seventy eight, seventy nine, eighty

eighty one, eighty two, eighty three, eighty four, eighty five, eighty six, eighty seven, eighty nine, ninety

ninety-one, ninety two, ninety three, ninety four, ninety five, ninety six, ninety seven, ninety eight, ninety nine, one hundred

Q5. Page 12

Hundreds	Tens	Units
	6	8
1	5	0
	3	9
	4	7
1	0	2
1	5	8
2	0	0
		7
1	1	9
	9	9
1	7	1

Q6. Page 12

a) 35   b) 70

Q7. Page 13

1	2	3	4	5	6	7	8	9	10
11	12	13	14	15	16	17	18	19	20
21	22	23	24	25	26	27	28	29	30
31	32	33	34	35	36	37	38	39	40
41	42	43	44	45	46	47	48	49	50
51	52	53	54	55	56	57	58	59	60
61	62	63	64	65	66	67	68	69	70
71	72	73	74	75	76	77	78	79	80
81	82	83	84	85	86	87	88	89	90
91	92	93	94	95	96	97	98	99	100

101	102	103	104	105	106	107	108	109	110
111	112	113	114	115	116	117	118	119	120
121	122	123	124	125	126	127	128	129	130
131	132	133	134	135	136	137	138	139	140
141	142	143	144	145	146	147	148	149	150
151	152	153	154	155	156	157	158	159	160
161	162	163	164	165	166	167	168	169	170
171	172	173	174	175	176	177	178	179	180
181	182	183	184	185	186	187	188	189	190
191	192	193	194	195	196	197	198	199	200

Q8. Page 13

20	111	99
39	120	171
74	160	118
80	175	124
47	134	107
95	186	200

Q9. Page 13

67 **sixty seven**
113 **one hundred and thirteen**
190 **one hundred and ninety**
200 **two hundred**
107 **one hundred and seven**
138 **one hundred and thirty eight**
109 **one hundred and nine**
172 **one hundred and seventy two**
101 **one hundred and one**

Q10. Page 14

£138 one hundred and thirty eight pounds
£119 one hundred and nineteen pounds
£200 two hundred pounds
£189 **one hundred and eighty nine** pounds
£107 **one hundred and seven** pounds
£144 **one hundred and forty four** pounds

Q11. Page 14

Forty eight

Q12. Page 14

Eighty eight

Q13. Page 14

Ninety nine

Q14. Page 15

Jasi is **twenty four** years old.
Heather is **twelve** years older than Enes.
How old will Enes be in two years' time? **Twenty**.

Q15. Page 15

Q16. Page 15

No, this is door number nineteen, not ninety.

Q17. Page 15

£135

Q18. Page 15

£198

Progress Check Page 16
Q1.

Hundreds	Tens	Units
	6	8
1	5	0
1	4	1
	3	5
	6	0
1	0	8
1	0	0
		9

Q2.

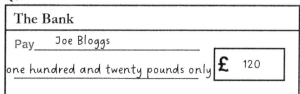

17	one hundred
100	sixty-eight
111	one hundred and eleven
68	seventeen

Q3. No, the number is eighteen.

Q4. Fifty-five

Q5.

The Bank	
Pay Joe Bloggs	
one hundred and twenty pounds only	£ 120

Order and compare numbers up to 200

Q1. Page 17

42 is **smaller** than 100
74 is **smaller** than 82
37 is **smaller** than 38
78 is **greater** than 62

Q2. Page 17

66 is **greater** than 58	0 is **smaller** than 43
49 is **smaller** than 85	12 is **smaller** than 70
19 is **smaller** than 67	27 is **smaller** than 29
100 is **greater** than 50	20 is **greater** than 19
91 is **smaller** than 100	50 is **smaller** than 54

Q3. Page 18

119 is **greater** than 100	109 is **smaller** than 110
160 is **greater** than 130	190 is **greater** than 180
108 is **smaller** than 180	109 is **smaller** than 120
17 is **smaller** than 117	160 is **greater** than 159
100 is **smaller** than 101	130 is **greater** than 0

Q4. Page 18

29 is **lower** than 129	200 is **higher** than 199
115 is **lower** than 150	159 is **higher** than 155
108 is **lower** than 140	169 is **lower** than 200
170 is **lower** than 194	186 is **lower** than 194
0 is **lower** than 176	135 is **higher** than 116

Q5. Page 18

77 or any other greater number.

Q6. Page 18

159 or any other smaller number.

Q7. Page 18

Any number between 77 and 159.

Q8. Page 18

No, 16 is smaller than 22.

Q9. Page 18

No, he needs £17 more.

Q10. Page 18

100 or any other greater number.

Q11. Page 18
79 or any other smaller number.

Q12. Page 18
Any number between 81 and 98.

Q13. Page 19
Out of 37, 40 and 54, **37** is the smallest and **54** is the greatest.
Out of 67, 53 and 100, **53** is the smallest and **100** is the greatest.
Out of 92, 90 and 86, **86** is the smallest and **92** is the greatest.
Out of 39, 0 and 44, **0** is the smallest and **44** is the greatest.
Out of 58, 72 and 82, **58** is the smallest and **82** is the greatest.
Out of 66, 16 and 60, **16** is the smallest and **66** is the greatest.
Out of 78, 41 and 29, **29** is the smallest and **78** is the greatest.

Q14. Page 20
a)90 b)195 c)198 d)160 e)196 f)60 g)18 h)100 i)74 j)105

Q15. Page 20
a) 57, 84, 103
b) 163, 196, 200
c) 40, 89, 104
d) 92, 167, 185
e) 153, 174, 187
f) 153, 184, 186
) 169, 170, 171
h) 110, 134, 177

Q16. Page 20
a) 192, 191, 167
b) 195, 180, 174
c) 172, 120, 100
d) 108, 100, 99
e) 200, 120, 20
f) 190, 118, 108
g) 169, 145, 137
h) 180, 137, 1

Q17. Page 20
a) 23, 31, 53, 82
b) 49, 67, 107, 188
c) 58, 95, 142, 162
d) 133, 119, 71, 26
e) 164, 145, 139, 108
f) 162, 120, 108, 91

Q18. Page 21
a) Ticket A   b) Ticket A, Ticket B, Ticket D, Ticket C

Q19. Page 21
187m, 170m, 80m, 78m

Q20. Page 21
Bag C

Q21. Page 21
a) Office A
b) Office A, Office C, Office B, Office D

Q22. Page 21
a) The £34 coat ticked
b) £34, £41, £52, £57

Q23. Page 21
Yes. 57 is lower than 60.

Progress Check Page 22
Q1. £180, £108, £81, £18

Q2.a)

The Bank	
Pay Joe Bloggs	
one hundred and twenty pounds only	£ 120

The Bank	
Pay Joe Bloggs	
one hundred and two pounds only	£ 102

b)

The Bank	
Pay Joe Bloggs	
one hundred and twenty pounds only	£ 120

Q3. No, should be: 18, 72, 91 103, 105

Q4. Bus

Q5. Yes, 80 is greater than 18.

Count in ones up to 100

Q1. Page 23

25	**26**	27	**28**	29	**30**	31	**32**	**33**	**34**
50	51	**52**	53	**54**	**55**	**56**	57	**58**	**59**
88	89	**90**	**91**	**92**	93	**94**	**95**	**96**	**97**
65	**66**	67	**68**	69	**70**	**71**	**72**	**73**	**74**
61	**62**	**63**	**64**	65	**66**	67	68	**69**	70
40	**41**	42	**43**	**44**	**45**	46	**47**	**48**	**49**

Q2. Page 23
a)68 b)79 c)47 or 48 d)99 e)0 f)50 g)100 h)89

Q3. Page 23
21, **22**, 23, **24**, 25, **26**, 27, **28**, 29, **30**
30, 31, **32**, 33, **34**, 35, **36**, 37, **38**
41, 42, **43**, 44, 45, **46**, 47, 48, **49**, 50
65, 66, 67, **68**, **69**, 70, **71**, **72**, 73
55, 56, **57**, 58, **59**, **60**, **61**, **62**, 63, **64**
73, **74**, 75, **76**, **77**, 78, **79**, **80**, 81, **82**
90, **91**, 92, **93**, **94**, **95**, 96, **97**, **98**, 99
92, **93**, **94**, **95**, 96, **97**, 98, **99**, 100

Q4. Pages 24 and 25

24 apples

32 pears

57 footballs

47 squares

41 triangles

48 cubes

70 cubes

93 cubes

80 cubes

74 cubes

Q5. Page 26

26 pears – yes

20 tomatoes – no

28 eggs – no

58 cans of tuna – yes

40 pots of noodles – no

40 tins of soup - yes

Q6. Page 27

Examples:

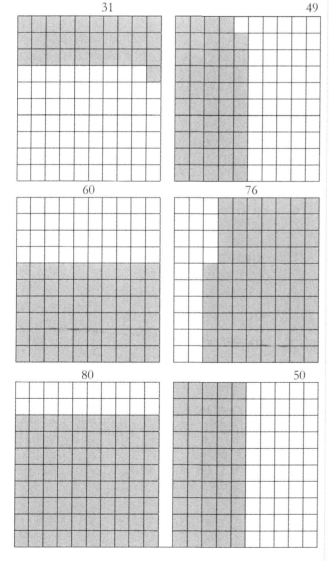

Q7. Page 28

100	99	98	97	96	95	94	93	92	91
90	89	88	87	86	85	84	83	82	81
80	79	78	77	76	75	74	73	72	71
70	69	68	67	66	65	64	63	62	61
60	59	58	57	56	55	54	53	52	51
50	49	48	47	46	45	44	43	42	41
40	39	38	37	36	35	34	33	32	31
30	29	28	27	26	25	24	23	22	21
20	19	18	17	16	15	14	13	12	11
10	9	8	7	6	5	4	3	2	1

Q8. Page 28

30	29	28	27	26	25	24	23	22	21
33	32	31	30	29	28	27	26	25	24
50	49	48	47	46	45	44	43	42	41
56	55	54	53	52	51	50	49	48	47
73	72	71	70	69	68	67	66	65	64
80	79	78	77	76	75	74	73	72	71
100	99	98	97	96	95	94	93	92	91
90	89	88	87	86	85	84	83	82	81

Q9. Page 29

52

Q10. Page 29

26

Q11. Page 29

Yes, you take away one when counting backwards.

Q12. Page 29

Should be 51, 50, 49, 48, 47

Q13. Page 29

a)46 - 42 = 4   b)90   c)80 or 81

Q14. Page 30

No, there are 28 files.

Progress Check Page 30

Q1. 23

Q2. No, she has 22 cubes.

Q3.

43, 44, 45, **46**, 47, **48, 49**, 50

Q4.

70, 71, 72, 73, 74, 75

Q5.

86, 52, 25, 16, 13, 10

Q6. No, 80 is missing.

Count in twos up to 100

Q1. Page 31

1p, 3p, 5p, **7p**, 9p, **11p**, **13p**, **15p**, **17p**, **19p**

Q2. Page 31

0, 2, **4**, 6, **8**, 10, **12**, 14, **16**, **18**, **20**

Q3. Page 31

six

Q4. Page 31

20	22	24	26	28	30	32	34	36	38
forty	forty two	**forty four**	**forty six**	forty eight	**fifty**	fifty two	**fifty four**	fifty six	**fifty eight**
61	63	65	**67**	69	**71**	73	**75**	77	**79**
eighty one	**eighty three**	eighty five	**eighty seven**	**eighty nine**	**ninety one**	ninety three	**ninety five**	ninety seven	**ninety nine**

Q5. Page 31

12, 14, **16**, 18, **20**, 22, **24**
30, **32**, 34, 36, **38**, **40**
65, **67**, **69**, **71**, 73, **75**
72, **74**, **76**, 78, **80**
88, **90**, **92**, 94, **96**, **98**
40, **42**, 44, 46, **48**, **50**

Progress Check Page 32

Q1. 42

Q2. 36

Q3. 52, 54, 56, **58**, 60, **62**, **64**, 66

Q4. 30, **32**, 34, 36, 38, 40

Q5. Yes: 9, 11, 13, 15, 17, 19, 21, 23, 25, 27, 29, 31.

Q6. No. Should be 43, 45, 47, 49 or 42, 44, 46, 48

Q7.

30, 31, **32**, 33, **34**, 35, **36**
50, **52**, 54, **56**, **58**, 60
88, **86**, 84, 82, **80**, 78
100, 99, **98**, 97, **96**, **95**, **94**
75, **77**, **79**, 81, 83, **85**
42, **44**, 46, **48**, **50**, **52**
68, **70**, **72**, 74, **76**, **78**
72, 71, **70**, 69, 68, 67

Counting in tens, twenties and fives, up to 100

Q1. Page 33
a) 10, **20**, 30, **40**, 50, **60**, 70
b) £10, £20, **£30**, **£40**, **£50**

Q2. Page 33
a) 20, **40**, 60, **80**, 100
b) £20, **£40**, £60, **£80**, £100

Q3. Page 34
£5, **£10**, **£15**, **£20**, **£25**, £30, **£35**, **£40**, **£45**, **£50**, **£55**, **£60**, £65, **£70**, **£75**

Q4. Page 34
5, 10, **15**, **20**, **25**, 30

Q5. Page 34
5, 10, 15, **20**, 25, **30**, 35
20, **25**, 30, 35, 40, **45**, 50
65, **70**, **75**, 80, 85, **90**

17, 27, 37, **47**, **57**, **67**
43, **53**, 63, **73**, **83**, 93
60, **70**, **80**, **90**, 100

20, **40**, **60**, **80**, 100
32, 42, **52**, **62**, **72**
0, 20, 40, **60**, 80, **100**

5, 15, 25, **35**, 45, **55**
39, 49, **59**, **69**, 79
95, 75, 55, **35**, **15**

Q6. Page 34
No, she has given 80p change.

Q7. Page 34
Missed 25.

Progress Check Page 35
Q1. 43 + 10 = 53

Q2. 67 - 20 = £47

Q3.
a) Yes. 30 is greater than 28.
b) Yes. 5, 10, 15, 20, 25, 30, 35
c) 10 boxes. 10, 20, 30, 40, 50, 60, 70, 80, 90, 100
d) Two tins.
e) Three.
f) £50
g) 100
h) 80
i) Should be 44, 54, 64, 74, 84
j) Should be 72, 62, 52, 42, 32, 22

Q4. Yes, when starting from 0 or 10, 20 etc.

Q5. Yes, when starting from 0 or 5, 10, 15, 30 etc.

Recognise and sequence odd and even numbers up to 100

Q1. Page 36
2, 4, **6**, **8**, **10**, **12**, **14**

Q2. Page 37
a) 1, 3, **5**, **7**, 9
b) 65, **67**, 69, **71**

Q3. Page 37

1	**2**	3	**4**	5	**6**	7	**8**	9	**10**
11	**12**	13	**14**	15	**16**	17	**18**	19	**20**
21	**22**	23	**24**	25	**26**	27	**28**	29	**30**
31	**32**	33	**34**	35	**36**	37	**38**	39	**40**
41	**42**	43	**44**	45	**46**	47	**48**	49	**50**
51	**52**	53	**54**	55	**56**	57	**58**	59	**60**
61	**62**	63	**64**	65	**66**	67	**68**	69	**70**
71	**72**	73	**74**	75	**76**	77	**78**	79	**80**
81	**82**	83	**84**	85	**86**	87	**88**	89	**90**
91	**92**	93	**94**	95	**96**	97	**98**	99	**100**

Q4. Page 38

1	2	**3**	4	**5**	6	**7**	8	**9**	10
11	12	**13**	14	**15**	16	**17**	18	**19**	20
21	22	**23**	24	**25**	26	**27**	28	**29**	30
31	32	**33**	34	**35**	36	**37**	38	**39**	40
41	42	**43**	44	**45**	46	**47**	48	**49**	50
51	52	**53**	54	**55**	56	**57**	58	**59**	60
61	62	**63**	64	**65**	66	**67**	68	**69**	70
71	72	**73**	74	**75**	76	**77**	78	**79**	80
81	82	**83**	84	**85**	86	**87**	88	**89**	90
91	92	**93**	94	**95**	96	**97**	98	**99**	100

Q5. Page 38
a) 7 or 9 or 11 or any other odd number greater than 5.
b) 12 or 10 or 8 or 6 or 4 or 2

Q6. Page 38

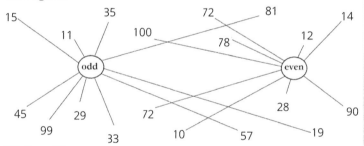

Q7. Page 38
No, 54 is even.

Q8. Page 38
No, 23 is odd.

Q9. Page 39
Odd

Q10. Page 39

7 + 5 = **12**	15 + 9 = **24**	23 + 17 = **40**
6 + 8 = **14**	10 + 14 = **24**	26 + 26 = **52**
9 + 12 = **21**	11 + 6 = **17**	21 + 34 = **55**
6 + 7 = **13**	12 + 7 = **19**	36 + 13 = **49**

odd	+	odd	=	**even**
even	+	even	=	**even**
odd	+	even	=	**odd**
even	+	odd	=	**odd**

Q11. Page 39
14

Q12. Page 39
Yes, 38 is even.

Progress Check Page 39
Q1.

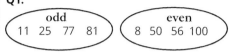

odd: 11 25 77 81   even: 8 50 56 100

Q2. 22, 24, 26, **28, 30, 32**

Q3. 37, 39, 41, 43, **45**

Q4. Yes. Example: 3 comes after 2; 5 comes after 4, etc

Q5. Yes, this is correct.

Add two-digit numbers

Q1. Pages 40 and 41
63 + 31 = 94
79 + 21 = 100
57 + 11 = 68
46 + 22 = 68
76 + 23 = 99
48 + 34 = 82
64 + 25 = 89
63 + 8 = 71
57 + 28 = 85
52 + 41 = 93
33 + 37 = 70
51 + 36 = 87

Q2. Page 42
84 + 25 = 109
57 + 53 = 110
92 + 46 = 138
89 + 42 = 131
73 + 67 = 140
63 + 94 = 157
99 + 99 = 198

Q3. Page 43
a) 20 + 10 = 30   7 + 2 = 9   30 + 9 = 39
b) 40 + 20 = 60   4 + 0 = 4   60 + 4 = 64
c) 50 + 20 = 70   5 + 9 = 14   70 + 14 = 84
d) 30 + 20 = 50   5 + 7 = 12   50 + 12 = 62
e) 60 + 30 = 90   4 + 2 = 6   90 + 6 = 96
f) 40 + 20 = 60   8 + 6 = 14   60 + 14 = 74

Q4. Page 44
a) 60 + 20 = 80   1 + 4 = 5   80 + 5 = 85
b) 80 + 10 = 90   6 + 1 = 7   90 + 7 = 97
c) 70 + 10 = 80   3 + 9 = 12   80 + 12 = 92
d) 20 + 20 = 40   4 + 5 = 9   40 + 9 = 49
e) 60 + 30 = 90   3 + 3 = 6   90 + 6 = 96
f) 70 + 20 = 90   5 + 6 = 11   90 + 11 = 101
g) 70 + 20 = 90   0 + 7 = 7   90 + 7 = 97
h) 60 + 20 = 80   2 + 3 = 5   80 + 5 = 85
i) 20 + 30 = 50   7 + 2 = 9   50 + 9 = 59
j) 40 + 50 = 90   4 + 9 = 13   90 + 13 = 103

Q5. Page 46

13 + 16 = 29	12 + 25 = 37	45 + 34 = 79	10 + 67 = 77	33 + 57 = 90	13 + 46 = 59	54 + 25 = 79
38 + 41 = 79	16 + 32 = 48	15 + 73 = 88	54 + 26 = 80	22 + 67 = 89	51 + 38 = 89	24 + 34 = 58
68 + 11 = 79	10 + 58 = 68	34 + 65 = 99	42 + 47 = 89	65 + 24 = 89	10 + 79 = 89	53 + 33 = 86
25 + 55 = 80	11 + 51 = 62	62 + 34 = 96	60 + 30 = 90	54 + 22 = 76	66 + 3 = 69	71 + 26 = 97
62 + 25 = 87	53 + 15 = 68	26 + 43 = 69	41 + 17 = 58	35 + 34 = 69	23 + 64 = 87	44 + 16 = 60

Q6. Page 51

91 + 67 = 158	24 + 85 = 109	56 + 84 = 140	90 + 87 = 177	93 + 73 = 166	13 + 96 = 109	14 + 57 = 71
48 + 81 = 129	76 + 27 = 103	15 + 72 = 87	84 + 26 = 110	26 + 77 = 103	91 + 38 = 129	64 + 74 = 138
41 + 48 = 89	70 + 58 = 128	54 + 82 = 136	72 + 57 = 129	65 + 74 = 139	92 + 19 = 111	53 + 83 = 136
95 + 25 = 120	31 + 75 = 106	62 + 76 = 138	59 + 10 = 69	14 + 27 = 41	86 + 57 = 143	58 + 96 = 154
42 + 85 = 127	73 + 35 = 108	16 + 73 = 89	78 + 11 = 89	47 + 31 = 78	68 + 69 = 137	80 + 95 = 175

Q7. Page 52
14 + 5 = **19**   23 + 8 = **31**   16 + 27 = **43**   59 + 14 = **73**
5 + 14 = **19**   8 + 23 = **31**   27 + 16 = **43**   14 + 59 = **73**

Q8. Page 52
26 + 38 = 64

Q9. Page 52
76 + 39 = £115

Q10. Page 52
43 + 64 = 107gb

Q11. Page 52
No. 25 + 60 + 25 = 110 minutes

Q12. Page 52
Yes. 15 + 0 = 15

Q13. Page 52
35 + 45 = £80

Q14. Page 52
72 + 95 = 167

Progress Check Page 53
1. 69 + 99 = 168p

2. 44 + 39 = 83

3.

27 + 15 = **42**	12 + **23** = 35	**70** + 9 = 79
44 + 26 = **70**	58 + **8** = 66	**79** + 14 = 93

4.
24 + 4 = 4 + 24 is correct
0 + 35 = 0 is not correct. It should be 0 + 35 = 35

5. Any two numbers that add up to 71.
Example: 24 + 47

6. 43 + 36 = 79

Subtract two-digit numbers

Q1. Pages 54 and 55
63 - 31 = 32
79 - 21 = 58
57 - 11 = 46
46 - 22 = 24
76 - 23 = 53
48 - 34 = 14
64 - 25 = 39
63 - 8 = 55
57 - 28 = 29
52 - 41 = 11
79 - 38 = 41
85 - 42 = 43
67 - 56 = 11

Q2. Page 56
a) 40 - 30 = 10   7 - 1 = 6   10 + 6 = 16
b) 60 – 40 = 20   8 – 5 = 3   20 + 3 = 23
c) 60 – 30 = 30   0 – 0 = 0   30 + 0 = 30
d) 80 – 60 = 30   9 – 3 = 6   30 + 6 = 36
e) 90 – 40 = 50   7 – 2 = 5   50 + 5 = 55
f) 40 – 30 = 10   4 – 3 = 1   10 + 1 = 11

Q3. Page 57
a) 30 – 20 = 10   5 – 3 = 2   10 + 2 = 12
b) 40 – 10 = 30   7 – 6 = 1   30 + 1 = 31
c) 90 – 40 = 50   7 – 2 = 5   50 + 5 = 55
d) 30 – 20 = 10   6 – 6 = 0   10 + 0 = 10
e) 60 – 60 = 0   8 – 4 = 4   0 + 4 = 4
f) 30 – 10 = 20   5 – 3 = 2   20 + 2 = 22
g) 50 – 40 = 10   9 – 1 = 8   10 + 8 = 18
h) 70 – 40 = 30   7 – 0 = 7   30 + 7 = 37
i) 30 – 20 = 10   7 – 6 = 1   10 + 1 = 11
j) 50 – 40 = 10   6 – 4 = 2   10 + 2 = 12

Q4. Page 61

41 − 7	64 − 45	75 − 34	80 − 47	73 − 37	53 − 26	94 − 66
34	**19**	**41**	**33**	**36**	**27**	**28**
68 − 41	66 − 62	45 − 33	84 − 46	92 − 57	65 − 29	64 − 24
27	**4**	**12**	**38**	**35**	**36**	**40**
41 − 28	50 − 38	64 − 42	62 − 37	75 − 54	80 − 69	83 − 63
13	**12**	**22**	**25**	**21**	**11**	**20**
35 − 25	41 − 21	42 − 22	60 − 10	44 − 27	96 − 67	71 − 46
10	**20**	**20**	**50**	**17**	**29**	**25**
72 − 35	63 − 25	46 − 33	78 − 67	55 − 43	53 − 46	60 − 55
37	**38**	**13**	11	12	7	5

Q5. Page 62

43 – 17 = 26

Q6. Page 62

a) 36 – 20= 16
b) 16 + 20 = 36

Q7. Page 62

Yes

Q8. Page 62

No, should be 24 – 4 = 20

Q9. Page 62

No, should be 68 + 24 = 92

Q10. Page 62

Yes. Example: 17 – 0 = 17

Q11. Page 63

9 + ___ = 14 is the same as **14 - 9**
5 + ___ = 12 is the same as **12 - 5**
8 + ___ = 19 is the same as **19 - 8**
___ + 5 = 14 is the same as **14 - 5**
___ + 7 = 12 is the same as **12 - 7**
___ + 11 = 19 is the same as **19 - 11**

Q12. Page 63

59 take away 28 is written as **59 - 28**
60 take away 11 is written as **60 - 11**
46 take away 34 is written as **46 - 34**
Take away 25 from 37 is written as **37 - 25**
Take away 9 from 44 is written as **44 - 9**
Take away 11 from 89 is written as **89 - 11**

Q13. Page 64

15 + 5 = 20 Checking: 20 – 5 = 15

Q14. Page 64

19 – 12 = 7 Checking: 7 + 12 = 19

Q15. Page 64

70 – 15 = £55 Checking: 55 + 15 = 70

Q16. Page 64

80 – 57 = 23 Checking: 23 + 57 = 80

Q17. Page 64

15 + 25 = 40 Checking: 40 – 25 = 15

Q18. Page 64

24 - 10 = 14 Checking: 14 + 10 = 24

Q19. Page 64

5 + 8 = 13 Checking: 13 – 8 = 5

Q20. Page 65

a) 20 – 5 = 15
b) 100 – 36 = 64
c) 72 – 54 = 18
d) 90 – 45 = 45

Q21. Page 65

a) 36 – 10 = 26
b) 11 + 14 = 25th
c) 9 + 27 = 36
d) 25 + 6 = £31
e) 7 + 7 + 7 = 21
f) 23 + 5 = 28 minutes
g) 46 + 15 = 61 years old
h) 27 + 36 = 63 minutes
i) 35 + 25 = 60
j) 64 + 64 = 128

Q22. Page 66

Example: 17 + 15 = 32
Example: 20 + 21 = 41
Example: 33 = 14 + 19
Example: 27 = 6 + 21
Example: 40 – 25 = 15
Example: 19 – 13 = 6
Example: 10 = 53 - 43
Example: 12 = 46 - 34

Q23. Page 66

Example: 22 + 22 = 44
Example: 4 + 40 = 44
Example: 44 = 10 + 34
Example: 44 = 17 + 27
Example: 45 – 32 = 13
Example: 82 – 69 = 13
Example: 13 = 26 - 13
Example: 13 = 59 - 46

Q24. Page 66

25 - 25 = 0	18 – 18 = 0	56 – 56 = 0
12 – 12 = 0	20 - 20 = 0	0 - 0 = 0

Q25. Page 66

+
6	8
2	**7**
9	5

+
2	8
3	5
6	**3**

+
3	4
4	**8**
8	2

+
2	3
3	**8**
6	1

Q26. Page 67

−
6	8
2	**3**
4	5

−
8	8
3	**9**
4	9

−
6	4
4	**7**
1	7

−
7	3
	4
6	9

Q27. Page 67

Numbers have not been aligned, with units under units and tens under tens.

Progress Check Page 67

Q1. 90 – 44 = 46p

Q2. 24 – 8 = 16

Q3.

39 - 5 = **34**	54 - 26 = **28**	55 - **43** = 12
76 - **68** = 8	**69** - 59 = 10	**86** - 4 = 82

Q4.

24 - 4 = 4 – 24 is not correct as order matters when subtracting

25 - 0 = 25 is correct as taking away 0 doesn't change the number

Q5. Example: 57 – 26

Q6.

8 + 8 = 16   Check: 16 – 8 = 8

8 + 6 = 14   Check: 14 – 6 = 8

5 + 12 = 17   Check: 17 – 12 = 5

9 + 6 = 15   Check: 15 – 6 = 9

<u>Multiply whole numbers in the range 0x0 to 12x12 (times tables)</u>

Q1. Page 69

0 x 6 = 0

Q2. Page 69

0 x 5 = 0

Q3. Page 69

1 x 10 = 10

Q4. Page 69

8 x 1 = £8

Q5. Page 70

5 x 2 = 10

Q6. Page 70

2 x 7 = 14 metres

Q7. Page 70

6 x 3 = £18

Q8. Page 70

3 x 9 = 27 metres

Q9. Page 70

3 x 4 = 12

Q10. Page 70

4 x 6 = £24

Q11. Page 71

12 x 5 = €60

Q12. Page 71

5 x 3 = 15

Q13. Page 71

4 x 6 = 24

Q14. Page 72

6 x 10 = £60

Q15. Page 72

6 x 7 = 42

Q16. Page 72

7 x 6 = 42

Q17. Page 72

8 x 5 = £40

Q18. Page 72

3 x 8 = £24

Q19. Page 72

9 x 12 = 108

Q20. Page 72

5 x 9 = £45

Q21. Page 73

10 x 10 = 100

Q22. Page 73

12 x 10 = £120

Q23. Page 73

6 x 11 = £66

Q24. Page 74

11 x 12 = £132

Q25. Page 74

12 x 12 = 144

Q26. Page 74

12 x 5 = £60

Q27. Page 74

1 x 0 = **0**	2 x 0 = **0**	3 x 0 = **0**	4 x 0 = **0**	5 x 0 = **0**	6 x 0 = **0**
1 x 1 = **1**	2 x 1 = **2**	3 x 1 = **3**	4 x 1 = **4**	5 x 1 = **5**	6 x 1 = **6**
1 x 2 = **2**	2 x 2 = **4**	3 x 2 = **6**	4 x 2 = **8**	5 x 2 = **10**	6 x 2 = **12**
1 x 3 = **3**	2 x 3 = **6**	3 x 3 = **9**	4 x 3 = **12**	5 x 3 = **15**	6 x 3 = **18**
1 x 4 = **4**	2 x 4 = **8**	3 x 4 = **12**	4 x 4 = **16**	5 x 4 = **20**	6 x 4 = **24**
1 x 5 = **5**	2 x 5 = **10**	3 x 5 = **15**	4 x 5 = **20**	5 x 5 = **25**	6 x 5 = **30**
1 x 6 = **6**	2 x 6 = **12**	3 x 6 = **18**	4 x 6 = **24**	5 x 6 = **30**	6 x 6 = **36**
1 x 7 = **7**	2 x 7 = **14**	3 x 7 = **21**	4 x 7 = **28**	5 x 7 = **35**	6 x 7 = **42**
1 x 8 = **8**	2 x 8 = **16**	3 x 8 = **24**	4 x 8 = **32**	5 x 8 = **40**	6 x 8 = **48**
1 x 9 = **9**	2 x 9 = **18**	3 x 9 = **27**	4 x 9 = **36**	5 x 9 = **45**	6 x 9 = **54**
1 x 10 = **10**	2 x 10 = **20**	3 x 10 = **30**	4 x 10 = **40**	5 x 10 = **50**	6 x 10 = **60**
1 x 11 = **11**	2 x 11 = **22**	3 x 11 = **33**	4 x 11 = **44**	5 x 11 = **55**	6 x 11 = **66**
1 x 12 = **12**	2 x 12 = **24**	3 x 12 = **36**	4 x 12 = **48**	5 x 12 = **60**	6 x 12 = **72**

7 x 0 = **0**	8 x 0 = **0**	9 x 0 = **0**	10 x 0 = **0**	11 x 0 = **0**	12 x 0 = **0**
7 x 1 = **7**	8 x 1 = **8**	9 x 1 = **9**	10 x 1 = **10**	11 x 1 = **11**	12 x 1 = **12**
7 x 2 = **14**	8 x 2 = **16**	9 x 2 = **18**	10 x 2 = **20**	11 x 2 = **22**	12 x 2 = **24**
7 x 3 = **21**	8 x 3 = **24**	9 x 3 = **27**	10 x 3 = **30**	11 x 3 = **33**	12 x 3 = **36**
7 x 4 = **28**	8 x 4 = **32**	9 x 4 = **36**	10 x 4 = **40**	11 x 4 = **44**	12 x 4 = **48**
7 x 5 = **35**	8 x 5 = **40**	9 x 5 = **45**	10 x 5 = **50**	11 x 5 = **55**	12 x 5 = **60**
7 x 6 = **42**	8 x 6 = **48**	9 x 6 = **54**	10 x 6 = **60**	11 x 6 = **66**	12 x 6 = **72**
7 x 7 = **49**	8 x 7 = **56**	9 x 7 = **63**	10 x 7 = **70**	11 x 7 = **77**	12 x 7 = **84**
7 x 8 = **56**	8 x 8 = **64**	9 x 8 = **72**	10 x 8 = **80**	11 x 8 = **88**	12 x 8 = **96**
7 x 9 = **63**	8 x 9 = **72**	9 x 9 = **81**	10 x 9 = **90**	11 x 9 = **99**	12 x 9 = **108**
7 x 10 = **70**	8 x 10 = **80**	9 x 10 = **90**	10 x 10 = **100**	11 x 10 = **110**	12 x 10 = **120**
7 x 11 = **77**	8 x 11 = **88**	9 x 11 = **99**	10 x 11 = **110**	11 x 11 = **121**	12 x 11 = **132**
7 x 12 = **84**	8 x 12 = **96**	9 x 12 = **108**	10 x 12 = **120**	11 x 12 = **132**	12 x 12 = **144**

Q28. Page 74

No, 5 x 7 = 35

Q29. Page 75

1 x 10 = **10**	2 x 0 = **0**	3 x 7 = **21**	5 x 0 = **0**	5 x 11 = **55**	6 x 3 = **18**
4 x 1 = **4**	8 x 1 = **8**	3 x 8 = **24**	4 x 6 = **24**	5 x 12 = **60**	6 x 2 = **12**
6 x 2 = **12**	7 x 2 = **14**	3 x 4 = **12**	4 x 8 = **32**	5 x 7 = **35**	6 x 6 = **36**
9 x 3 = **27**	4 x 3 = **12**	9 x 3 = **27**	4 x 3 = **12**	5 x 5 = **25**	6 x 4 = **24**
8 x 4 = **32**	9 x 4 = **36**	4 x 4 = **16**	4 x 9 = **36**	6 x 4 = **24**	6 x 8 = **48**
3 x 5 = **15**	6 x 5 = **30**	8 x 5 = **40**	4 x 6 = **24**	5 x 5 = **25**	6 x 9 = **54**
6 x 6 = **36**	2 x 6 = **12**	5 x 6 = **30**	7 x 6 = **42**	3 x 6 = **18**	6 x 10 = **60**
9 x 7 = **63**	3 x 7 = **21**	3 x 7 = **21**	9 x 7 = **63**	8 x 7 = **56**	8 x 7 = **56**
4 x 8 = **32**	6 x 8 = **48**	9 x 8 = **72**	11 x 8 = **88**	4 x 8 = **32**	9 x 8 = **72**
6 x 9 = **54**	4 x 9 = **36**	2 x 9 = **18**	1 x 9 = **9**	9 x 9 = **81**	4 x 9 = **36**
5 x 10 = **50**	6 x 10 = **60**	10 x 10 = **100**	12 x 10 = **120**	4 x 10 = **40**	9 x 10 = **90**
9 x 11 = **99**	7 x 11 = **77**	6 x 11 = **66**	4 x 11 = **44**	6 x 11 = **66**	7 x 11 = **77**
10 x 12 = **120**	2 x 12 = **24**	12 x 12 = **144**	4 x 12 = **48**	8 x 12 = **96**	5 x 12 = **60**

Q30. Page 75

x	0	1	2	3	4	5	6	7	8	9	10	11	12
0	0	0	0	0	0	0	0	0	0	0	0	0	0
1	0	1	2	3	4	5	6	7	8	9	10	11	12
2	0	2	4	6	8	10	12	14	16	18	20	22	24
3	0	3	6	9	12	15	18	21	24	27	30	33	36
4	0	4	8	12	16	20	24	28	32	36	40	44	48
5	0	5	10	15	20	25	30	35	40	45	50	55	60
6	0	6	12	18	24	30	36	42	48	54	60	66	72
7	0	7	14	21	28	35	42	49	56	63	70	77	84
8	0	8	16	24	32	40	48	56	64	72	80	88	96
9	0	9	18	27	36	45	54	63	72	81	90	99	108
10	0	10	20	30	40	50	60	70	80	90	100	110	120
11	0	11	22	33	44	55	66	77	88	99	110	121	132
12	0	12	24	36	48	60	72	84	96	108	120	132	144

Q31. Page 75

Yes, 3 x 12 = 36

Q32. Page 75

Yes. Example: 5 x 0 = 0

Q33. Page 75

3 x **5** = 15	6 x **7** = 42	7 x **3** = 21
6 x **4** = 24	5 x **4** = 20	8 x **6** = 48

3 x 3 = 9	**7** x 5 = 35	**7** x 11 = 77
6 x 6 = 36	**4** x 9 = 36	**10** x 12 = 120

Q34. Page 76

a)) 3 x 6 = £18
b) 5 x 5 = 25
c) 10 x 1 = 10kg
d) 4 x 2 = 8kg
e) No, 2 x 3 = 6
f) No. 3 x 4 = 12
g) Yes. 5 x 2 = £10
h) 6 x 6 = 36
i) 3 x 4 = 12   12 – 10 = 2   So, 2 more.

Q35. Page 76

2, 4, 6, **8, 10, 12, 14, 16, 18, 20, 22, 24**

5, 10, 15, **20, 25, 30, 35, 40, 45, 50, 55, 60**

7, 14, 21, 28, 35, 42, 49, **56, 63, 70, 77, 84**

4, 8, 12, 16, 20, 24, 28, 32, 36, 40, **44, 48**

9, 18, 27, 36, 45, **54, 63, 72, 81, 90, 99, 108**

6, 12, 18, 24, 30, 36, 42, 48, 54, 60, 66, 72

8, 16, 24, **32, 40, 48, 56, 64, 72, 80, 88, 96**

3, 6, 9, 12, 15, 18, **21, 24, 27, 30, 33, 36**

11, 22, 33, 44, 55, 66, 77, 88, 99, 110, 121, 132

Q36. Page 76

Yes, she has split four into two and two and multiplied each by eight.

Q37. Page 77

2 x 10 is the same as 10 x **2**
12 x 4 is the same as 4 x **12**
5 x 6 is the same as 6 x **5**
11 x 3 is the same as **3** x 11
7 x 8 is the same as 8 x **7**

Progress Check Page 77

Q1. 3 x 6 = 18

Q2. 9 x 12 = 108

Q3.

5 x 10 = **50**	4 x **8** = 32	**6** x 6 = 36

Q4.

6 x 4 = 4 x 6 is correct

1 x 5 = 1 is wrong. Should be 1 x 5 = 5

5 x 0 = 5 is wrong. Should be 5 x 0 = 0

Q5. Example: 4 x 6

Divide two-digit whole numbers by single-digit whole numbers and express remainders

Q1. Page 79

10 ÷ 2 = **5**	40 ÷ 4 = **10**	24 ÷ 6 = **4**	42 ÷ 6 = **7**	63 ÷ 7 = **9**
15 ÷ 5 = **3**	32 ÷ 8 = **4**	16 ÷ 4 = **4**	64 ÷ 8 = **8**	100 ÷ 10 = **10**
21 ÷ 3 = **7**	16 ÷ 2 = **8**	18 ÷ 3 = **6**	81 ÷ 9 = **9**	40 ÷ 5 = **8**

Q2. Page 82

46 ÷ 2 = **23**	93 ÷ 3 = **31**	84 ÷ 4 = **21**	84 ÷ 2 = **42**	55 ÷ 5 = **11**	60 ÷ 6 = **10**
66 ÷ 2 = **33**	63 ÷ 3 = **21**	48 ÷ 4 = **12**	90 ÷ 3 = **30**	77 ÷ 7 = **11**	88 ÷ 2 = **44**
39 ÷ 3 = **13**	50 ÷ 5 = **10**	82 ÷ 2 = **41**	96 ÷ 3 = **32**	88 ÷ 4 = **22**	66 ÷ 3 = **22**

Q3. Page 82

a) 36 ÷ 3 = £12

b) 30 ÷ 3 = 10

c) 55 ÷ 5 = 11

d) 84 ÷ 4 = 21

e) 69 ÷ 3 = 23

f) 26 ÷ 2 = 13

Q4. Page 82

Answer is 20. Should do how many lots of three fit into 6 and then into 0.

Q5. Page 85

56 ÷ 2 = **28**	72 ÷ 3 = **24**	96 ÷ 4 = **24**	94 ÷ 2 = **47**	75 ÷ 5 = **15**	84 ÷ 6 = **14**
96 ÷ 2 = **48**	84 ÷ 3 = **28**	60 ÷ 4 = **15**	87 ÷ 3 = **29**	91 ÷ 7 = **13**	54 ÷ 2 = **27**
48 ÷ 3 = **16**	90 ÷ 5 = **18**	96 ÷ 2 = **48**	57 ÷ 3 = **19**	56 ÷ 4 = **14**	72 ÷ 2 = **36**

Q6. Page 85

a) 42 ÷ 3 = £14

b) 48 ÷ 3 = 16

c) 65 ÷ 5 = 13

d) 72 ÷ 4 = 18

e) 78 ÷ 3 = 26

f) 36 ÷ 2 = 18

Q7. Page 85

Answer is 24. Should do how many lots of three fit into 7 and then into 12.

Q8. Page 88

57 ÷ 2 = **28 r 1**	74 ÷ 3 = **24 r 2**	98 ÷ 4 = **24 r 2**	95 ÷ 2 = **47 r 1**	77 ÷ 5 = **15 r 2**	87 ÷ 6 = **14 r 3**
97 ÷ 2 = **48 r 1**	85 ÷ 3 = **28 r 1**	61 ÷ 4 = **15 r 1**	88 ÷ 3 = **29 r 1**	97 ÷ 7 = **13 r 6**	55 ÷ 2 = **27 r 1**
50 ÷ 3 = **16 r 2**	93 ÷ 5 = **18 r 3**	97 ÷ 2 = **48 r 1**	59 ÷ 3 = **19 r 2**	59 ÷ 4 = **14 r 3**	49 ÷ 3 = **16 r 1**

Q9. Page 88

a) 86 ÷ 7 = 12 rem 2   12 pairs

b) 50 ÷ 3 = 16 rem 2   16 pens

c) 35 ÷ 4 = 8 rem 3   8 pies

d) 75 ÷ 4 = 18 rem 3   19 packs

e) 67 ÷ 5 = 13 rem 2   13 buses

f) 37 ÷ 2 = 18 rem 1   18 pieces

Q10. Page 88

The answer is 24 rem 2. 24.2 is not the same as 24 rem 2.

Q11. Page 90

a) 12 ÷ 3 = 4

b) 80 ÷ 2 = 40p

c) 18 ÷ 6 = 3

d) 20 ÷ 5 = 4

e) 9 ÷ 3 = 3

f) 50 ÷ 5 = £10

g) 10 ÷ 1 = 10

h) 60 ÷ 5 = 12

Q12. Page 90

Yes, she is correct. 13 x 4 = 52

Q13. Page 90

No, should be: 54 ÷ 3 = 18

Q14. Page 90

Yes, she is correct. 11 x 8 = 88

Q14. Page 90

Yes, she is correct. 12 ÷ 3 = 4

Q16. Page 91

No, dividing by 0 gives you no answer (is undefined).

Q17. Page 91

9 x ___ = 27 is the same as **27 ÷ 9**

5 x ___ = 20 is the same as **20 ÷ 5**

8 x ___ = 32 is the same as **32 ÷ 8**

___ x 5 = 35 is the same as **35 ÷ 5**

___ x 7 = 42 is the same as **42 ÷ 7**

___ x 11 = 66 is the same as **66 ÷ 11**

Q18. Page 91

3 x 4 = 12 so 12 ÷ 3 = **4** and 12 ÷ 4 = **3**

7 x 5 = 35 so 35 ÷ 5 = **7** and 35 ÷ 7 = **5**

6 x 8 = 48 so 48 ÷ 6 = **8** and 48 ÷ 8 = **6**

4 x 7 = 28 so 28 ÷ 4 = **7** and 28 ÷ 7 = **4**

Q19. Page 92

27 + 25 = 52   Checking: 52 – 25 = 27

Q20. Page 92

84 – 38 = 46   Checking: 46 + 38 = 84

Q21. Page 92

90 ÷ 5 = 18   Checking: 18 x 5 = 90

Q22. Page 92

12 x 8 = 96 Checking: 96 ÷8 = 12

Q23. Page 92

7 x 12 = 84 Checking: 84 ÷ 7 = 12

Q24. Page 93

30 ÷ 3 = 10 Checking 10 x 3 = 30

Q25. Page 93

18 + 18 = 36   Check: 36 – 18 = 18
28 - 16 = 12   Check: 12 + 16 = 28
5 x 4 = 20   Check: 20 ÷ 4 = 5
29 + 36 = 65   Check: 65 – 36 = 29
10 + 68 = 78   Check: 78 – 68 = 10
42 ÷ 7 = 6   Check: 6 x 7 = 42
56 ÷ 8 = 7   Check: 7 x 8 = 56
37 - 6 = 31   Check: 31 + 6 = 37

Q26. Page 93

Yes, she is correct.

Q27. Page 93

No, should be 84 ÷ 12 = 7

Progress Check Page 93
Q1.
15 ÷ 6 = 2 rem 3   3 packs
Checking: 2 x 6 = 12   12 + 3 = 15

Q2. 64 ÷ 4 = £16

Q3.

36 ÷ 9 = **4**	50 ÷ 10 = **5**	63 ÷ **9** = 7	64 ÷ 7 = **9r1**

Q4.
16 ÷ 4 = 4 ÷ 16 is wrong. Order matters when dividing
5 ÷ 1 = 1 is wrong.
Dividing a number by 1 gives us the number itself.
So: 5 ÷ 1 = 5

Q5. 6 x 7 = 42 or 7 x 6 = 42

Recognise and interpret symbols for + , - , x , ÷ and = appropriately

Q1. Page 94

6 + 4 = 10	8 + 3 = 11	6 ÷ 2 = 3	4 x 3 = 12	8 - 4 = 4
10 - 4 = 6	17 – 2 = 15	16 ÷ 2 = 8	3 x 3 = 9	20 + 20 = 40
12 + 3 = 15	10 + 0 = 10	4 x 4 = 16	20 - 20 = 0	24 ÷ 4 = 6
15 - 3 = 12	15 + 5 = 20	15 + 5 = 20	72 ÷ 8 = 9	8 + 4 = 12

Q2. Page 94
47 + 33

Q3. Page 94
33 - 16

Q4. Page 94
71 - 46

Q5. Page 95
35 ÷ 5 = 7

Q6. Page 95
4 x 4 = £16

Q7. Page 95
35 ÷ 5 = 7

Q8. Page 95
6 x 7 = 42

Q9. Page 95
50 – 32 = 18

Q10. Page 95
a) ÷
b) x

Q11. Page 95

Subtract		More
Makes	+	Equals
Total		Left over
Lots of	-	Plus
Add		And
Take away	=	Share equally
Divide		Subtract from
Minus	÷	Altogether
Times	x	Multiply

Q12. Page 96

53 + 48 = **101**	93 - 54 = **39**	56 - 37 = **19**
63 + 67 = **130**	47 - 26 = **21**	70 + 10 = **80**

0 x 12 = **0**	10 x 10 = **100**	12 ÷ 3 = **4**
40 ÷ 5 = **8**	12 x 8 = **96**	42 ÷ 7 = **6**

Q13. Page 96

48 + 68 = **116**	63 - 44 = **19**	45 + 72 = **117**
50 + 30 = **80**	87 - 25 = **62**	76 - 39 = **37**

4 x 9 = **36**	10 x 10 = **100**	18 ÷ 3 = **6**
45 ÷ 5 = **9**	7 x 8 = **56**	42 ÷ 3 = **14**

Q14. Page 96
46 – 11 = 35

Q15. Page 96
35 – 28 = 7

Q16. Page 96
9 x 7 = 63

Q17. Page 97
28 ÷ 7 = £4

Q18. Page 97
7 x 10 = 70

Q19. Page 97
98 ÷ 7 = 14

Q20. Page 97

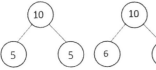

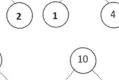

Q22. Page 98

35 + 10 = 45
45 − 1 = 44

56 + 30 = 86
86 - 3 = 83

77 + 30 = 107
107 - 2 = 105

42 − 20 = 22
22 + 2 = 24

77 − 10 = 67
67 + 1 = 68

56 − 30 = 26
26 + 1 = 27

Q21. Page 98

1 + **4** = 5	2 + **3** = 5	**1** + 4 = 5	**0** + 5 = 5	**2** + 3 = 5
3 + **2** = 5	4 + **1** = 5	**3** + 2 = 5	3 + 2 = **5**	**4** + 1 = 5
0 + **10** = 10	1 + **9** = 10	**3** + 7 = 10	**10** + 0 = 10	2 + **8** = 10
3 + **7** = 10	4 + **6** = 10	**4** + 6 = 10	**8** + 2 = 10	5 + **5** = 10
6 + **4** = 10	7 + **3** = 10	**6** + 4 = 10	**1** + 9 = 10	8 + **2** = 10

Q23. Page 99

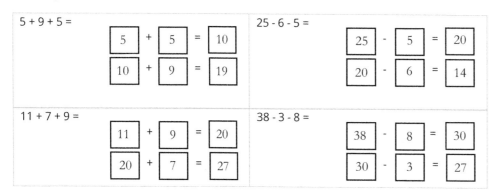

5 + 9 + 5 =	25 - 6 - 5 =
5 + 5 = 10 10 + 9 = 19	25 - 5 = 20 20 - 6 = 14
11 + 7 + 9 =	38 - 3 - 8 =
11 + 9 = 20 20 + 7 = 27	38 - 8 = 30 30 - 3 = 27

Progress Check Page 99
Q1.

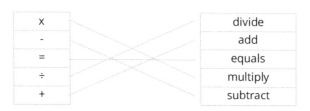

x		divide
-		add
=		equals
÷		multiply
+		subtract

Q2.

6 + 5 = 11	12 ÷ 4 = 3	20 − 8 = 12
2 **x** 7 = 14	12 ÷ 3 = 4	5 ÷ 5 = 1

Q3.

x   times, **multiply**, lots of
÷   **divide**, share equally, **split**

Q4. 5 = 10 ÷ 2

Q5. 80 − 50 = 30p

Q2. Page 101
30 + 40 + 10 = £80

Q3. Page 101
60 − 40 = 20

Q4. Page 101
4 x 20 = 80

Q5. Page 101
50 ÷ 10 = 5

Q6. Page 101
65 − 18 = 47
Checking: **70 - 20 = 50**

11 + 57 = 68
Checking: **10 + 60 = 70**

93 − 3 = 90
Checking: **90 − 0 = 90**

64 + 25 = 89
Checking: **60 + 30 = 90**

59 − 46 = 23
Checking: **60 − 50 = 20**

10 + 19 + 55 = 84
Checking: **10 + 20 + 60 = 90**

75 − 29 = 46
Checking: **80 − 30 = 50**

Q7. Page 101
40 ÷ 10 = 4

Q8. Page 102
10 x 10 = 100

Q9. Page 102
15, 16, 17, 18, 19, 20, 21,
22, 23, 24

Approximate by rounding to the nearest 10, and use this answer to check results

Q1. Page 101

83	**80**	19	**20**	4	**0**	27	**30**	35	**40**	50	**50**
76	**80**	54	**50**	90	**90**	99	**100**	12	**10**	75	**80**
63	**60**	71	**70**	24	**20**	68	**70**	66	**70**	5	**10**

Q10. Page 102

75, 76, 78, 79, 80, 81, 82, 83, 84

Q11. Page 102

a) 44 + 38 = £82

b) £80

Q12. Page 102

a) £10

b) 10 x 10 = £100

Q13. Page 102

50 + 60 = £110

Q14. Page 102

a) 59 + 74 = £133

b) 60 + 70 = £130

Progress Check Page 103

Q1. 76 + 92 = £168

Q2.

a) 81 + 19 + 55 = £155

b) 80 + 20 + 60 = 160

Q3. 55, 56, 57, 58, 59, 60, 61, 62, 63, 64

Q4. Yes. 30 to the nearest ten is 30.

Q5.

a) 40

b) 0

c) 100

Recognise simple fractions (halves, quarters and tenths) of whole numbers and shapes

Q1. Page 104

Q2. Page 105

a) 8 ÷ 2 = 4 slices

b) 6 ÷ 2 = 3 sweets

c) 10 ÷ 2 = 5 eggs

d) 10 ÷ 2 = £5

Q3. Page 105

No, the parts should be equal in size.

Q4. Page 105

$\frac{1}{2}$ of 8	$\frac{1}{2}$ of 16	$\frac{1}{2}$ of 60	$\frac{1}{2}$ of 22	$\frac{1}{2}$ of 32
4	8	30	11	16
$\frac{1}{2}$ of 10	$\frac{1}{2}$ of 2	$\frac{1}{2}$ of 100	$\frac{1}{2}$ of 18	$\frac{1}{2}$ of 200
5	1	50	9	100
$\frac{1}{2}$ of 4	$\frac{1}{2}$ of 20	$\frac{1}{2}$ of 30	$\frac{1}{2}$ of 40	$\frac{1}{2}$ of 80
2	10	15	20	40

Q5. Page 106

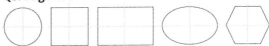

Q6. Page 106

Yes, all parts are equal in size.

Q7. Page 106

a) 8 ÷ 4 = 2 slices

b) 12 ÷ 4 = 3 sweets

c) 16 ÷ 4 = 4 cans of tuna

d) 20 ÷ 4 = £5

Q8. Page 107

$\frac{1}{4}$ of 8	$\frac{1}{4}$ of 16	$\frac{1}{4}$ of 60	$\frac{1}{4}$ of 24	$\frac{1}{4}$ of 32
2	4	15	6	8
$\frac{1}{4}$ of 12	$\frac{1}{4}$ of 40	$\frac{1}{4}$ of 100	$\frac{1}{4}$ of 36	$\frac{1}{4}$ of 200
3	10	25	9	50
$\frac{1}{4}$ of 4	$\frac{1}{4}$ of 20	$\frac{1}{4}$ of 28	$\frac{1}{4}$ of 44	$\frac{1}{4}$ of 80
1	5	7	11	20

Q9. Page 107

18 is $\frac{1}{2}$ of 36	4 is $\frac{1}{4}$ of 16	7 is $\frac{1}{2}$ of 14

Q10 Page 107

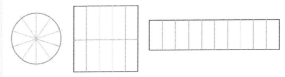

Q11. Page 107

100 ÷ 10 = 10

Q12. Page 108

a) 20 ÷ 10 = £2

b) 40 ÷ 10 = 4 sweets

c) 10 ÷ 10 = 1 egg

d) 120 ÷ 10 = £12

Q13. Page 108

$\frac{1}{10}$ of 30	$\frac{1}{10}$ of 70	$\frac{1}{10}$ of 60	$\frac{1}{10}$ of 90
3	7	6	9
$\frac{1}{10}$ of 10	$\frac{1}{10}$ of 40	$\frac{1}{10}$ of 100	$\frac{1}{10}$ of 120
1	4	10	12
$\frac{1}{10}$ of 50	$\frac{1}{10}$ of 20	$\frac{1}{10}$ of 80	$\frac{1}{10}$ of 110
5	2	8	11

Q14. Page 108

80 ÷ 4 = 20

Q15. Page 108

60 ÷ 4 x 3 = 45

Q16. Page 109

a) 28 ÷ 4 = 7

b) 84 ÷ 2 = 42g

c) $\frac{1}{10}$

d) 20 ÷ 10 = 2

Q17. Page 109

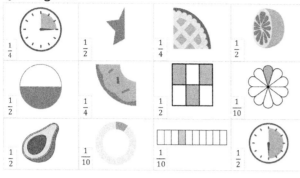

Q18. Page 110

No, 16 ÷ 4 = 4

Q19. Page 110

Yes. Example: 8 ÷ 4 = 2 is the same as 8 ÷ 2 ÷ 2 = 2

Q20. Page 110

a) 2

b) 5

Q21. Page 110

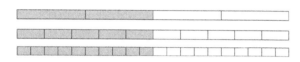

Q22. Page 111

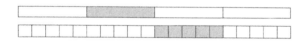

Q23. Page 111

Q24. Page 111

a) $\frac{1}{2}$

b) $\frac{1}{2}$, $\frac{1}{4}$, $\frac{1}{10}$

Progress Check Page 112

Q1.

Q2. Yes, $\frac{1}{4}$ means 1 out 4.

Q3.

Fraction in digits	Fraction in words
$\frac{1}{10}$	one quarter
$\frac{1}{2}$	half
$\frac{1}{10}$	one tenth

Q4.

$\frac{1}{2}$ of 64 is 32 and $\frac{1}{4}$ of 100 is 25. So $\frac{1}{2}$ of 64 is greater.

Q5.

30 ÷ 2 = £15

Q6.

No $\frac{1}{2}$ means splitting something into two parts, $\frac{1}{4}$ means splitting it into four equal parts.

Read, write and use decimals to one decimal place

Q1. Page 113

3.4 --- three point four

16.7 --- sixteen point seven

0.9 --- zero point nine

10.0 --- ten point zero

140.3 --- one hundred and forty point three

Q2. Page 113

7 + 0.6 = 7.6	10 + 0.6 = 10.6	23 + 0.9 = 23.9	0.1 + 14 = 14.1	99 + 0.2 = 99.2	101 + 0.7 = 101.7

Q3. Page 114

1	1.1	1.2	1.3	1.4	1.5	1.6	1.7	1.8	1.9	2
0	0.1	0.2	0.3	0.4	0.5	0.6	0.7	0.8	0.9	1
5	5.1	5.2	5.3	5.4	5.5	5.6	5.7	5.8	5.9	6
10	10.1	10.2	10.3	10.4	10.5	10.6	10.7	10.8	10.9	11

Q4. Page 114

| 7 | 7.1 | 7.2 | 7.3 | 7.4 | 7.5 | 7.6 | 7.7 | 7.8 | 7.9 | 8 |

Q5. Page 114

| 12 | 12.1 | 12.2 | 12.3 | 12.4 | 12.5 | 12.6 | 12.7 | 12.8 | 12.9 | 13 |

Q6. Page 114

| 0 | 0.1 | 0.2 | 0.3 | 0.4 | 0.5 | 0.6 | 0.7 | 0.8 | 0.9 | 1 |

Q7. Page 114

Q8. Page 114

Q9. Page 115

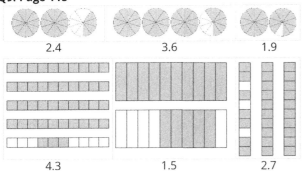

2.4   3.6   1.9

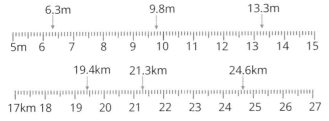

4.3   1.5   2.7

Q10. Page 115

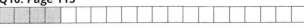

Q11. Page 116

6.3m   9.8m   13.3m

5m 6 7 8 9 10 11 12 13 14 15

19.4km   21.3km   24.6km

17km 18 19 20 21 22 23 24 25 26 27

10.2kg   14.1kg   19.9kg

10kg 11 12 13 14 15 16 17 18 19 20

Q12. Page 116

1.5, 6, 0.8

Q13. Page 116

a) 0.1
b) 0.3
c) 0.1

Q14. Page 116

0.7, 0.8. 1, 1.8

Q15. Page 117

3.1	2.4	5.6	5.0	1.3	1.3	1.4
+ 6.7	+ 6.5	+ 2.4	+ 3.7	+ 7.3	+ 8.6	+ 5.7
9.8	8.9	8.0	8.7	8.6	9.9	7.1
4.8	7.6	1.5	8.4	2.6	9.1	6.4
+ 4.1	+ 1.7	+ 7.2	+ 2.6	+ 7.7	+ 3.8	+ 7.4
8.9	9.3	8.7	11.0	10.3	12.9	13.8

Q16. Page 117

9.7	8.5	8.6	9.0	9.3	9.3	5.7
- 6.1	- 8.4	- 5.4	- 8.7	- 7.3	- 4.6	- 4.5
3.6	0.1	3.2	0.3	2.0	4.7	1.2
8.1	7.6	7.2	8.4	7.6	9.1	7.4
- 4.8	- 2.7	- 5.1	- 2.6	- 2.7	- 3.8	- 6.8
3.3	4.9	2.1	5.8	4.9	5.3	0.6

Q17. Page 118

a) 1.9kg, 2.4kg, 10.0kg, 10.6kg
b) 1 + 1.5 = 2.5kg
c) Friday 4.6km
d) 0.5 + 0.5 = 1 litre
e) A 2.3m
f) 0.8 – 0.5 = 0.3m

Q18. Page 118

2.1 as it has 2 units/ones.

Q19. Page 118

34.7 – 12.4 = 22.3 litres

Q20. Page 119

2.3 – 1.7 = 0.6 litres

Progress Check Page 119

Q1.

Q2.

a) 1.6 + 1.6 = 3.2m
b) Yes, 3.2 is greater than 3.0

Q3.

Decimal in digits	Decimal in words
0.6	zero point six
4.9	**four point nine**
10.8	ten point eight

Q4.

3.7 and 7.3 have the same digits but 7.3 is greater as it has 7 ones/units.

Q5.

a) 45.7, 47.5, 54.7, 57.4, 74.5, 75.4
b) 45.7, 47.5, 54.7, 57.4, 74.5, 75.4

Calculate money with pence up to one pound and in whole pounds of multiple items and write with correct symbols (£ and p)

Q1. Page 120

1p   2p   5p   £1   50p   20p   10p   £2

Q2. Page 120

1p   2p   5p   £1   20p   10p   £2   50p

Q3. Page 121

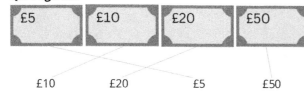

£10 £20 £5 £50

Q4. Page 121

1 penny --- 1p   20 pounds --- £20
2 pounds --- £2   5 pounds --- £5
5 pence --- 5p   10 pounds --- £10
10 pence --- 10p   50 pence --- 50p

Q5. Page 121

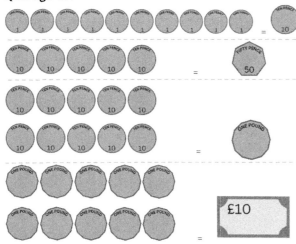

Q6. Page 122

Q7. Page 121

Q8. Page 121
£1

Q9. Page 122
81p

Q10. Page 122
a) 18 + 3 = £21
b) 30 – 21 = £9

Q11. Page 122
a)

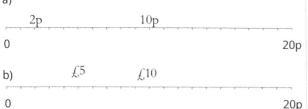

b)

Q12. Page 122
a) 18 + 26 = £44 Change: 50 – 44 = £6
b) No, it's 37 pounds, not pence.
c) The pound should be put in front of the amount: £17
d) 39 + 39 = £78
e) 27 + 19 = £46, so 50 – 46 = £4
f) No, it's 50 dollars, not pounds.
g) No, she spent £9, not 9p.
h) You can only write £15 for 15 pounds or 15p for 15 pence, not both symbols at the same time.

Progress Check Pages 124 and 125
Q1. a)

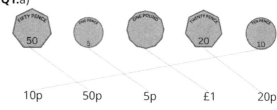

10p 50p 5p £1 20p

b) 5p, 10p, 20p, 50p, £1

Q2.
a) 22 + 36 = 58p
b) 100 – 58 = 42p
c) No, it's 42p. 42p + 58p = £1

Q3.

19p + 43p = **62p**	66p – 34p = **32p**	**28p** + 72p = £1
35p + **65p** = £1	79p – **10p** = 69p	£1 – 58p = **42p**

Q4.
She has not aligned them correctly.
Should be:

```
      56p
  +   29p
  _____
```

Q5. a)

£20 £50 £5 £10

b) £5, £10, £20, £50

Q6.
a) 58 + 79 = £137
b) 180 – 137 = £43

Q7.

£19 + £43 = **£62**	£35 + **£65** = £100	£79 – **£10** = £69	£66 – £34 = **£32**

Q8. She is adding pence and pounds.

Q9. 1p, 2p, 5p, 10p, 50p, £5, £10, £20

Know the number of hours in a day and weeks in a year. Be able to name and sequence them

Q1. Page 126
24

Q2. Page 126

2 days

Q3. Page 126

24 + 24 + 24 = 72

Q4. Page 126

a) 7

b) 5

Q5. Page 126

No, 12pm is midday.

Q6. Page 127

December

Q7. Page 127

January

Q8. Page 127

52 – 6 = 46

Q9. Page 127

52 x 1 = 52

Q10. Page 128

52 + 52 = 104

Q11. Page 128

52 ÷ 2 = 26

Q12. Page 128

No, there are 24 hours in a day.

Q13. Page 128

No, there are more than 4 weeks in a month.

Q14. Page 128

52 + 52 = 104

Progress Check Page 128

Q1. 52

Q2. 24

Q3. 12am

Q4. 12am

Q5. 12

Q6. January

Q7.

a) 52 – 36 = 16

b) 36 + 36 + 36 = 108

Q8. 52 – 11 = 41

Read and record time in common date formats, and read time displayed on analogue clocks in hours, half hours and quarter hours, and understand hours from a 24-hour digital clock

Q1. Page 129

eighth of August

thirteenth of February

twenty-seventh of December

second of June

Q2. Page 130

_____10th March 2023_____

_____19th September 2007_____

_____2nd November 2011_____

_____22nd April 1995_____

_____13th October 1976_____

_____30th July 1963_____

_____17th May 2025_____

_____23rd August 2027_____

Q3. Page 130

08.05.25

8th May 25

08.05.25

20.08.27

20th August 27

20.08.2025

Q4.Page 131
a) Saturday
b) Thursday
c) Tuesday
d) Saturday
e) Monday
f) Monday
g) Tuesday
h) Monday

Q5. Page 132
30

Q6. Page 132
31

Q7. Page 132
a) 9th September
b) 13th June 2021
c) February
d) 30th January
e) 28.06.23
f) No, it's 31st January 2020

Q8. Page 134

1 : 00   10 : 00   6 : 00   7 : 00

Q9. Page 134

12 : 15   1 : 15   5 : 15   10 : 15

Q10. Page 134

8 : 15   5 : 15   9 : 15   3 : 15

Q11. Page 134

2 : 30   12 : 30   3 : 30   5 : 30

Q12. Page 135

8 : 30   1 : 30   10 : 30   6 : 30

Q13. Page 135

1 : 45   7 : 45   3 : 45   5 : 45

Q14. Page 135

2 : 45   9 : 45   1 : 45   8 : 45

Q15. Page 135

Q16. Page 136

11 : 30   6 : 15   8 : 45   5 : 30

1 : 00   12 : 15   10 : 45   9 : 15

Q17. Page 136

Q18. Page 136
a) No, it's quarter past eight.
b) No, it's quarter past nine.

Q19. Page 137

quarter past nine	quarter past ten	**quarter to ten**	**forty-five past nine**	**nine forty-five**

216

Q20. Page 137

quarter past eleven	half past eleven	quarter to eleven	**fifteen past eleven**	**eleven fifteen**

Q21. Page 137

quarter past twelve	half past eleven	**thirty past twelve**	**twelve thirty**	forty five past twelve

Q22. Page 137
8:45

Q23. Page 137
11:15

Q24. Page 137
7:45 + 1:15 = 9:00

Q25. Page 138

11 o'clock   6 o'clock   5 o'clock   2 o'clock   9 o'clock

Q26. Page 139

2 o'clock   9 o'clock   5 o'clock   11 o'clock   6 o'clock

Q27. Page 139

Q28. Page 139

Q29. Page 139

Q30. Page 139

Q31. Page 139
14:30 – 9:30 = 5:00 So, 5 hours.

Q32. Page 140
a) No, it's half an hour early.
b) 5 hours
c) 4:30
d) 7.5 hours
e) 11:00
f) 19:00

g) 11:15 in the morning
h) No, there are 60 minutes in one hour.
i) Two
j) 6.5
k) 21:00

Progress check Page 141
Q1.
a) October
b) 1980

Q2.
17.02.2023;   17.02.23;   17th Feb 23

Q3.

7 : 00   8 : 30   5 : 15   12 : 45

Q4.

11 o'clock   4 o'clock   9 o'clock   9 o'clock   7 o'clock

Q5.

Q6. No, should be 02.04.2020

Q7. 3:30 + 2:30 = 6:00 in the evening or 18:00

Q8. 9:00 + 8:00 = 17:00

Use metric measures of length including millimetres, centimetres, metres and kilometres

Q1. Page 142
7cm
10cm
6cm
12cm
8cm
15cm
11cm
13cm

Q2. Page 143
17cm

Q3. Page 143
85cm

Q4. Page 143
59cm, 60cm, 62cm, 63cm

Q5. Page 143
0.5m

Q6. Page 144
16.2cm

Q7. Page 144
70mm because the others are not long enough.

Q8. Page 144
1.9m

Q9. Page 144
1.5m

Q10. Page 145
80cm

Q11. Page 145

kilometre	millimetre	metre	centimetre
km	**mm**	**m**	**cm**

Q12. Page 145
Millimetre, centimetre, metre, kilometre

Q13. Page 145
C, B, A, D

Q14. Page 145
1.3 + 0.7 = 2.0km or 2km

Q15. Page 146
6.2km, 7.5km, 8.9km, 10.1km

Q16. Page 146
3.7 + 3.7km = 7.4km

Q17. Page 146
11.8 ÷ 2 = 5.9km

Q18. Page 146
a) 3m
b) 2cm
c) 20mm
d) 80cm

Q19. Page 146
Should be 20km.

Q20. Page 146
Should be **2m tall**.

Q21. Page 147
Yes. 4.0 is equal to 4.

Q22. Page 147
2.0 – 1.2 = 0.8m

Progress Check Page 147
Q1.
The short form of writing millimetre is **mm**.
The short form of writing kilometre is **km**.
The short form of writing **metre** is m.
The short form of writing **centimetre** is cm.

Q2. 110cm

Q3. 1mm, 1cm, 1m, 1km

Q4. 13cm

Q5. 46 + 46 = 92cm

Use metric measures of weight including grams and kilograms

Q1. Page 148

kilogram	gram
kg	**g**

Q2. Page 148
1 kilogram

Q3. Page 148
50 kilograms, 5 kilograms, 50 grams, 5 grams

Q4. Page 149

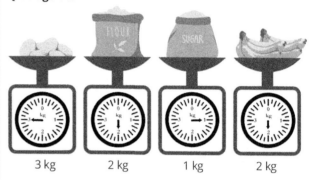

3 kg   2 kg   1 kg   2 kg

Q5. Page 149
19.8kg, 20.9kg, 21.0kg, 22.5kg

Q6. Page 148

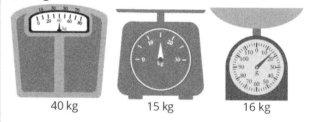

40 kg   15 kg   16 kg

Q7. Page 150
1.5kg and 1.9kg

Q8. Page 150
a) 10kg
b) 100g
c) 1g
d) 200g

Q9. Page 150
100 – 65 = 35g

Q10. Page 150
No, 17.8 + 82.5 = 100.3kg

Q11. Page 150
Should be 20kg.

Q12. Page 150
Yes, 10.0 is equal to 10.

Q13. Page 151
Yes, 30 + 30 + 30 + 7 = 97g

14. Page 151
No, it's 65g.

Progress Check Page 151
Q1.
The short form of writing gram is **g**.
The short form of writing **kilogram** is kg.

Q2. 7kg or 7.1kg

Q3. 1g, 50g, 1kg, 50kg

Q4. No, a thousand grams are equal to 1kg.

Q5. £6

Q6. 3.5 + 1.7 + 2.9 = 8.1kg

Use metric measures of capacity including millilitres and litres

Q1. Page 152
litre   millilitre
 l   **ml**

Q2. Page 152
1 litre

Q3. Page 152
5o litres, 5 litres, 50 millilitres, 5 millilitres

Q4. Page 153

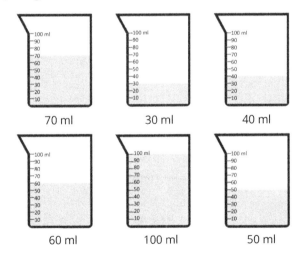

70 ml   30 ml   40 ml

60 ml   100 ml   50 ml

Q5. Page 153
15 ÷ 5 = 3

Q6. Page 153
12 ÷ 1.5 = 8

Q7. Page 153
1.5 ÷ 0.4 = 3.75 So, 4 cans of soup.

Q8. Page 154
a) 20 + 70 = 90ml
b) $\frac{1}{2}$
c) 12 x 1 = 12 litres
d) 0.5 + 0.5 + 0.5 + 0.5 = 2 litres. So, 4 bottles.
e) No, it holds more than 100ml.
f) 15 ÷ 2 = 7.5 So 7 bottles

Q9. Page 154
Yes, 12.0 is equal to 12.

Q10. Page 155
a) 1 litre
b) 100 millilitres
c) 10 litres

Q11. Page 155
70 litres, 7 litres, 70 millilitres, 7 millilitres

Q12. Page 155
70 + 93 = 163 ml

Q13. Page 155
Yes, 8 x 12 = 96 litres

Q14. Page 155
Should be 100 litres.

Q15. Page 155
95 – 35 = 60ml

Q16. Page 155
B 50 ml

Progress Check Page 156
Q1.
The short form of writing litre is **l** .
The short form of writing **millilitre** is ml.

Q2.

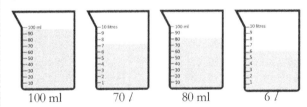

100 ml   70 l   80 ml   6 l

Q3. B 50 ml

Q4. 80 – 60 = 20ml

Q5. 98 ÷ 2 = 49ml

Q6. A 100 ml

Q7. 125ml, 45ml, 30ml, 25ml

Q8. 30 + 30 + 30 = 90ml. So, 3 cups.

Q9. B 55 ml

Q10. $\frac{1}{4}$

Read and compare positive temperatures

Q1. Page 157
24°C

Q2. Page 157
22 – 18 = 4°C

Q3. Page 158

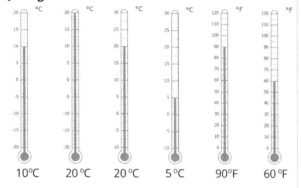

10°C   20°C   20°C   5°C   90°F   60°F

Q4. Page 158
a) 36.6°C
b) Yes, between 36°C and 37.5°C the body temperature is normal.

Q5. Page 158
a) B
b)

Q6. Page 159
a) Both thermometers show the same temperature.
b) B shows as a higher temperature than A.

Q7. Page 159
No, it's nearly 40°C.

Q8. Page 159
a) 15 + 8 = 23°C
b) 70 – 10 = 60°F

Progress Check Page 160
Q1.
The short form of writing 20 degree Celsius is **20°C**.
Water boils at **100**°C. Water **freezes** at 0°C.

Q2.

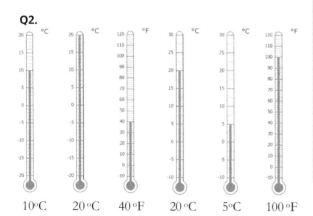

10°C   20°C   40°F   20°C   5°C   100°F

Q3.
a) No, should be 2 degrees lower.
b) 6 – 4 = 2°C

Q4. 18 – 15 = 3°C

Q5. 27 – 20 = 7°C

Q6. 2 – 2 = 0°C

Read and use simple scales to the nearest labelled division

Q1. Page 161

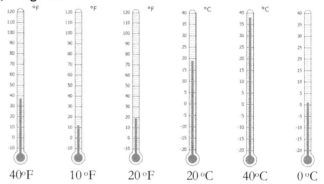

40°F   10°F   20°F   20°C   40°C   0°C

Q2. Page 162
a)

b) 30°C   80°F

Q3. Page 162
Yes, it's half-way between 26 and 27, so to the nearest cm it is 27.

Q4. Page 162
26cm
17cm

Q5. Page 162
No, it is 26cm.

Q6. Page 162
88.5, 88.6. 88.7, 88.8. 88.9, 89.0, 89.1, 89.2, 89.3, 89.4

Q7. Page 163

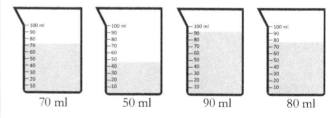

70 ml   50 ml   90 ml   80 ml

Q8. Page 163

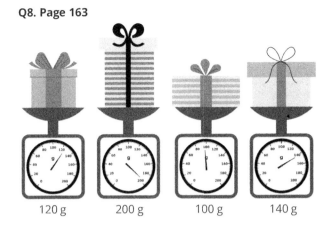

120 g   200 g   100 g   140 g

Q9. Page 163

a) 80kg

b) No, it's 0 litres.

Progress Check Page 164

Q1.

a) 45 – 30 = 15ml

b.i) 12cm   b.ii) No. it doesn't fit as 12 is greater than 10.

c) 7kg

d)

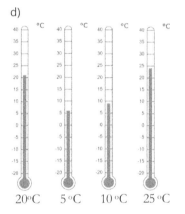

20°C   5°C   10°C   25°C

e) 25 + 1.5 + 1.5 = 28cm

Recognise and name common 2D and 3D shapes including pentagons, hexagons, cylinders, cuboids, pyramids and spheres

Q1. Page 165

square   rectangle   circle   triangle   pentagon   hexagon

Q2. Page 165

Hexagon

Q3. Page 166

pentagon   triangle   rectangle   circle   square   hexagon

Q4. Page 166

a)

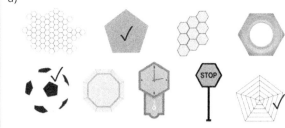

b) hexagons

Q5. Page 166

9 - 6 = 3

Q6. Page 167

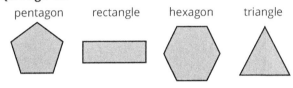

pentagon   rectangle   hexagon   triangle

Q7. Page 167

Shape names written again and again for practice.

Q8. Page 167

Q9. Page 167

pentagon

Q10. Page 167

Q11. Page 168

| cone | sphere | cube | cuboid | pyramid | cylinder |

Q12. Page 168

pyramid   sphere   cuboid   cube   cone   cylinder

Q13. Page 169

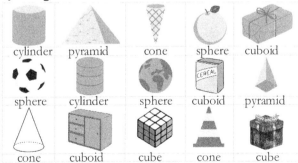

cylinder   pyramid   cone   sphere   cuboid

sphere   cylinder   sphere   cuboid   pyramid

cone   cuboid   cube   cone   cube

Q14. Page 169

Shape names written again and again for practice.

Q15. Page 169

2D Shape	3D Shapes
square	cuboid
pentagon	cube
hexagon	pyramid
rectangle	sphere
circle	cone
triangle	cylinder

Q16. Page 169

cube   cuboid   cylinder   pyramid   cone   sphere

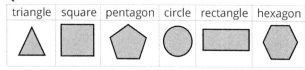

Progress Check Page 170

Q1.

triangle	square	pentagon	circle	rectangle	hexagon

Q2. 7 – 3 = 4

Q3. No, it's a rectangle.

Q4. No, it's a circle.

Q5. Cuboid

Describe the properties of common 2D and 3D shapes including number of sides, corners, edges, faces, angles and base

Q1. Page 171
a) square and rectangle
b) triangle
c) circle

Q2. Page 171

Q3. Page 171
rectangle

Q4. Page 172
a) cube and cuboid
b) sphere
c) cube and cuboid
d) cylinder
e) 6 faces
f) 3 faces
g) 12 edges
h) circle
i) 8 edges

Q5. Page 172
cuboid

Q6. Page 172
a) rectangle
b) yes

Q7. Page 173

Progress Check Page 173
Q1.

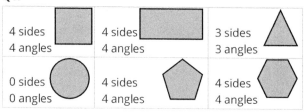

4 sides 4 angles	4 sides 4 angles	3 sides 3 angles
0 sides 0 angles	4 sides 4 angles	4 sides 4 angles

Q2.
square and rectangle

Q3.

Q4.

Cube	**Cylinder**	**Cuboid**
6 faces	3 faces	6 faces
12 edges	2 edges	12 edges
base: square	base: circle	base: rectangle or base
Cone	**Sphere**	**Pyramid**
2 faces	1 face	5 faces
1 edge	0 edges	8 edges
base: circle	base: none	base: square

Q5.
Yes

Q6.
No, it has 8 edges.

Use appropriate positional vocabulary to describe position and direction including between, inside, outside, middle, below, on top, forwards and backwards

Q1. Page 174
The bird is **on top of** the tree.
The ball is **below** the tree.
The cube is **on top of** the cuboid.
The cuboid is **below** the cube.
The plant is **on top of** the bookshelf.
The books are **below** the plant.

222

Q2. Page 175
The onion is **outside** the box.
The potatoes are **inside** the box.
The teddy bear is **inside** the toy box.
The car is **outside** the toy box.
The folded clothes are **outside** the basket.
The unfolded clothes are **inside** the basket.

Q3. Page 175
If the car moves **backwards**, it will hit the tree.
If the car moves **forwards**, it will hit the house.
When the minutes hand moves **forwards**, this is clockwise.
When the minutes hand moves **backwards**, this is anti-clockwise.
The boy is moving **backwards**.

Q4. Page 175
The clock is on the **middle** shelf.
The plant is on the **top** shelf.
The clock is **between** the plant and the mug.
The picture is in the **middle** .
The clock is on **top**.
The picture is **between** the clock and the mirror.

Q5. Page 176
a)
The bag is on top of **the shelf** .
The computer is below **the shelf** .
The computer is **between** the lamp and the pens.
The computer is in the middle.

b)
The bathroom is inside **the house**.
The car is outside the house.
The loft is on the **top** floor.

c) No, should be 'move forwards and then turn right'.

Progress Check Page 176
Q1.
The sphere is **on top** of the cylinder.
The cylinder is **between** cube and the cuboid.
The cube is **below** the cylinder.
The shape **in the middle** is called a cylinder.

Q2.a)
The glasses are **inside** the cupboard.
The cooking pot is **outside** the cupboard.

b)
If the bike moves **backwards**, it will hit the tree.
If the bike moves **forwards**, it will hit the lamppost.

Extract information from lists

Q1. Page 177
a) £42
b) the shoes
c) the belt
d) the belt
e) £1

Q2. Page 177
a)
i) Tuesday and Thursday
ii) Wednesday
iii) nature walk

b)
i) chocolate chip cookie and chocolate eclair
ii) five
iii) raspberry tart

Progress Check Page 178
Q1.
a) £10
b) £5
c) the alarm clock
d) £4
e) 4 ÷ 2 = £2
f) £31

Q2.
a) £5
b) 5 – 3 = £2
c) 10-3 = £7
d) Grilled Cheese Sandwich (Vegetarian)   £3

Q3.
a) 15:00
b) Gate 94
c) Glasgow
d) Nice

Extract information from tables

Q1. Page 179
a) Monday
b) Tuesday
c) physics
d) IT
e) chemistry
f) IT
g) 9-11am
h) 9-11am
i) 6-8pm

Q2. Page 179
a) 20°C
b) Wednesday
c) Thursday

Q3. Page 179
a) City C
b) City D
c) 55
d) 55 – 38 = 17

Progress Check Page 180
Q1.
a) 10
b) under 15 and 15-20
c) 20 – 10 = 10

d)

e) 160

Q2.

a) 17:00

b) Wednesday

Q3.

a) Book A

b) 195

c) 200 – 120 = 80

Q4.

a) Cloudy

b) Tuesday

c) 2

d)

Day	Weather
Monday	Sunny
Tuesday	Rainy
Wednesday	Cloudy
Thursday	Sunny
Friday	**Rainy**

Extract information from diagrams

Q1. Page 181

a) 24

b) Two

c) The kitchen is in between **the hall** and **the conference room**.

Progress Check Page 182

Q1.

a) Route 01

b) Two

c) Fireheart Canyon, Snowy Mountain, Emberfall Heights

Q2.

a) $\frac{1}{4}$

b) veggies

Extract information from bar charts

Q1. Page 183

a) 19

b) 23

c) Class A

Q2. Page 183

a) 92

b) 56

c) week 4

Progress Check Page 184

Q1.

a) 34

b)

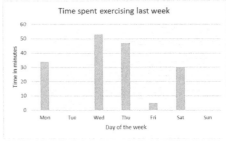

c) Wednesday

d) Saturday

e) Tuesday and Sunday

Q2.

a) Tuesday and Friday

b) Monday

c) Friday

Prevent referrals by age in winter 2021-2022	
Age	**Number of case (to the nearest 10)**
Under 15	60
15-20	60
21-30	20
31-40	10
41 and over	**10**

Make numerical comparisons from bar charts

Q1. Page 185

a) 56 – 34 = 22

b) February and March

c) February

Q2. Page 185

a) 2022

b) 78 – 52 = 26

c) 2021 and 2022

d) He is reading more every year.

Q3. Page 186

a) metal

b) 38 – 16 = 22

c) glass

d) glass

Q4. Page 186

a) 78

b) Yes

c) 78 – 65 = 13

d) No, 78 ÷ 2 = 39 or 65 + 65 = 130

Progress Check Page 187

Q1.

a) April and May

b) April

Q2.

a) Class B, Class C and Class D

b) Class C and Class D

Sort and classify objects using two criteria

Q1. Page 188

Q2. Page 189

Q3. Page 190
White cuboids

Q4. Page 190
15 and 19

Q5. Page 190
Three

Q6. Page 190

	healthy	unhealthy
food		
drinks		

Q1.

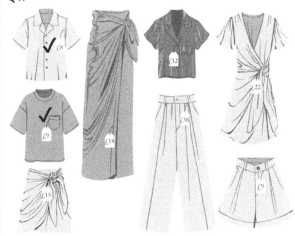

Q2. Grey 3D shapes

Q3. No, 16 is greater than 15 but even.

Take info from one format and represent the information in another format including the use of bar charts

Q1. Page 192

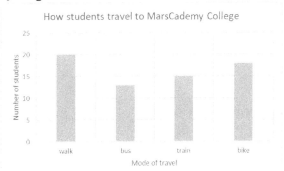

Q2. Page 193

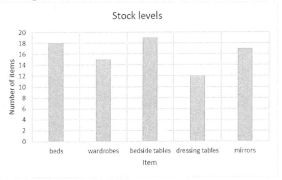

Q3. Page 193

Month	Number of items sold
Jan	78
Feb	81
Mar	85
Apr	81
May	90
Jun	93

Q4. Page 193

1. There is no title.
2. The axes are not labelled.
3. The scale is wrong

Progress Check Page 194

Q1.

Prevent referrals by age in winter 2021-2022	
Age (in years)	Number of cases (rounded to the nearest 10)
Under 15	60
15-20	60
21-30	20
31-40	10
41 and over	10

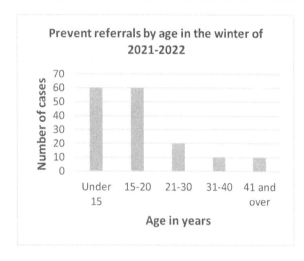

Practice Paper Part A Page 195

Q1. Eighty one

Q2.
43 + 86   (1 mark)
129   (1 mark)

Q3.
No   (1 mark)
50 – 36 = £14   (1 mark)

Q4.
No   (1 mark)
It's 3 o'clock.   (1 mark)

Practice Paper Part B Page 196

Q1. 24

Q2. 5 x 12 =

Q3. 55, 81, 101, 120

Q4.
20 ÷ 6 = 3 rem 2   (1 mark)
4 cartons   (1 mark)

Q5.
Hexagon

Q6.
69   (1 mark)
71   (1 mark)

Q7. 68

Q8.

Q9.

b) 7 – 6 = 1

Q10.

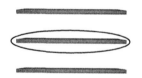

Q11.
a)
100 ÷ 4   (1 mark)
£25   (1 mark)
b) 100 – 25 = £75

Q12. 52 – 48 = 4 weeks

Q13.

Q14. No, this is less than 70ml.

Q15. Wednesday and Thursday

Getting 16 marks or more in the practice paper, means you have passed it.

If you don't get 16 marks or more, go back and revisit topics you lost marks in and retry the paper.

More practice papers can be found on **marscademy.com**

Printed in Great Britain
by Amazon